ROTOGR

Specialist publishers of price guide refere

CW00346829

Collectors' C
Decimal Issues of the United Kingdom

(formerly <u>Check Your Change</u>)

By Chris Henry Perkins.

2nd Edition © 2015

ISBN (printed version): 978-0-948964-60-2
ISBN (eBook version): 978-0-901170-35-4

A comprehensive UK decimal coin catalogue with values, descriptions and photographs

Special thanks to Lance Corporal M Mckerlie & Matthew Ahrens

Errors and Omissions:

Every effort has been made to ensure that the information and price data contained within this book are accurate and complete. However, errors do sometimes have a habit of creeping in unnoticed, and with this in mind the following email address has been established for notifications of omissions and errors: info@rotographic.com. Readers within the UK can also call the telephone number below.

Rotographic International

www.rotographic.com
020 308 69996

In Association with
predecimal.com

TABLE OF CONTENTS

INTRODUCTION

LISTINGS

INTRODUCTION

Welcome to the "Collectors' Coins - Decimal Issues of the UK" 2015 edition.

This inexpensive book, with listings and colour pictures of every decimal coin type should provide an excellent guide to modern coinage and as such, should aid existing collectors and hopefully stimulate new ones.

Decimal coinage first appeared forty-seven years ago (the florin and shilling being replaced by the Ten Pence and Five Pence respectively, in 1968) but is often overlooked as it has yet to stand the test of time in the same way that the pounds, shillings and pence did. As time progresses, interest in decimal coinage has increased and with this new interest will come a need for reference material. This book is designed to begin the process of compiling in-depth records of the modern money minted by the Royal Mint. Hopefully it will become a fundamental reference guide.

This book used to be 'Check Your Change' (originally published in the mid 1960s) but as decimals have been with us for two generations and most of the types are not seen in general circulation, this title has now morphed into a comprehensive guide to UK decimal coins. Together with it's sister "Collectors' Coins" publication, both books cover UK coinage from George III to date.

NEW IN 2015

It's been an interesting year for decimal coins. Since the last edition of this book it has been announced that a new bimetallic 12-sided £1 coin is due in 2017, to replace the current round and familiar coins that have been with us since 1983 and it seems are widely forged by criminal gangs. To replace all of the current £1 coins in circulation with an all-new high tech £1 coin is a massive task and I would imagine that the existing coins will probably remain in circulation for a while before they are all ultimately all replaced with the 12-sided new coin.

Also coming in March 2015 (probably already with us by the time this book becomes available) is a new aged portrait of the Queen to replace the current one which has been in use since 1998. I assume this new portrait introduction will mean that most or even all of the 2015 coins will be struck showing two different portraits of the Queen.

The 2015 battle of Britain commemorative 50p, which has so far been sold in the Royal Mint packs (in various guises) seems to have no marked denomination! I'm quite sure a coin with no marked denomination cannot possibly be legal tender. When the Royal Mint were asked about this they insisted that it was deliberate (I have my doubts about that!) and that the battle of Britain commemorative 50p that will be released into circulation (i.e. not the ones in the sets) will have a marked denomination and will feature the new portrait of the Queen.

Rare coin media frenzies seem to be a growing phenomenon these days They are not a new thing by any means (the same kind of thing happened in the 1960s with, for example 1950 and 1951 pennies) but the difference now is that the 'news' explodes onto the scene so much faster. Combine that with the ability that everyone has to sell things on the internet instantly and to large audiences and it means that whenever one of these media frenzies occurs that there is usually a spike in value for the coin involved as people speculate and demand is temporarily much greater than it was before. We saw this in 2008 with the undated error (mule) 20p and the huge prices those coins were selling for at the height. It happened again after it was reported that the Kew Gardens 50p was the 50p with the lowest mintage number, even though the number of coins struck is plenty to go round (the facts quoted were not entirely true either because the number struck is much higher if you also include the coins in sets and presentation packs). Something similar happened to the 2002 Commonwealth games Northern Ireland coin when it was established that this particular coin had the lowest mintage of any circulating £2 coin, even though the mintage figures were known for over ten years (and published in the predecessor of this book, for example).

Prices for the 1992-1993 EU 50p commemorative have also rocketed because this coin happens to have the lowest mintage number of the older large 50p coins, even though this fact was known for 20 years and prices were never particularly high!

And just recently it was reported that just 100 of the 2015 Royal Navy commemorative £2 coin were circulated to people visiting HMS Belfast on the Thames! Apparently no more coins of this design will be circulated because when the large numbers are struck for use they will feature the new portrait of the Queen. There was no mention of the very large amounts of these coins that already exist in the 2015 year-sets and in the presentation packs! And as usual, within a very short time they were on eBay described (like most things on eBay) as RARE etc. So far though, there has been less of a fuss about them than the previous stories instigated for the mule 20p and the Kew 50p, so perhaps the public have wised up to these sensational press releases.

New in this edition is full coverage of the £20 coin, which seems to have been so popular that the Royal Mint are now making a new design £20 coin each year. Another entirely new coin (and as far as I can tell, also without the actual real legal tender status that the Royal Mint imply) is the silver £100 coin featuring the clock-face of the tower known to most as Big Ben. Also covered in more detail for the first time are the 2009-2010 set of 18 £5 crown coins that were issued to celebrate Britishness and also feature the London 2012 logo.

USING THIS CATALOGUE

The values listed in this catalogue are the result of many hours of compiling and comparing the prices offered by online dealers, online auctions, dealer sales lists, live-auction catalogues, and other sources. For some items, there is such a limited number of transactions on which to base the values that they may seem conservative.

Values are in the main, only given for coins in uncirculated condition. The reason for this is that with the high mintage figures of virtually all coins covered in this catalogue, any coin that is not in uncirculated grade usually has virtually no value above the face value. There are exceptions though and where certain coins in used condition have a value above face value this is clearly shown in the listing under the 'Used' column.

MINTAGES

The numbers given as mintages are based on information available from many sources, including other reference works, online sources, and the Royal Mint. The accuracy of these numbers is by no means guaranteed, and modifications may be made as better information becomes available. It should also be noted that for some of the later issues, the mintages given are the "maximum mintages", and the actual number of pieces struck may be currently unknown. Again, updates will be made when final information is available.

COIN GRADES

The listings in this catalogue contain three prices, where applicable. The guidelines for these grades are as follows:

Used - A coin from circulation with normal wear and the usual bumps and scrapes from use. Most coins are just worth face value in used condition but for those that consistently sell for more than face value a 'Used' column is shown.

Uncirculated (UNC) - Appears as it did when it left the Mint. There will be no signs of wear or handling. May show "bag marks", as is common for mass-produced coins.

Brilliant uncirculated (BU) - A high end uncirculated. Fewer "bag marks" visible. All of, or 95%+ of the mint lustre remaining. Most coins from Specimen folders or sealed packaging are considered BU.

Proof - A coin usually struck from specially prepared coin dies on a specially prepared metal blank. Because of this extra care, Proofs usually exhibit much sharper detail and have mirror-like blank areas. Some proof coins show frosted design details.

THE VALUE OF GOLD

The price of gold influences the gold coin prices quoted in this book. The prices quoted here are based on a gold value of about £777 per ounce (£25,000 per kilogramme).

What's currently legal tender?
No half pennies are legal tender any longer. They were demonetised on the 31st December 1984. Banks do accept them, but the high street financial institutions are not exactly falling over themselves to exchange the half-pee tiddlers!

Which are hard to find?
The 1972 coin was made as a proof only and went into sets, so is harder to find. The last coin, dated 1984 was also made for sets only.

OBVERSE

OBVERSE 1
(used 1971 - 1984)
D•G•REG•F•D•(date) || ELIZABETH II
Elizabeth II, Dei Gratia Regina, Fidei Defensor
(Elizabeth II, By the Grace of God Queen and Defender of the Faith)
Portrait by: Arnold Machin

REVERSE

REVERSE 1
(used 1971 - 1981)
Regal Crown
½ NEW PENNY
Design by: Christopher Ironside

REVERSE 2
(used 1982 - 1984)
Regal Crown
½ HALF PENNY
Design by: Christopher Ironside

INFO
Although it was known from the onset that the half-penny would see limited circulation, it was necessary to help facilitate the transition from 'old money' to decimal, as the old sixpence coins were still circulating as 2½ new pence.

TYPE 1 (obverse 1, reverse 1)

		UNC	BU	Proof
1971	1,394,188,250	£0.05	£0.20	£2.00
1972	Proof Only			£5.00
1973	365,680,000	£0.10	£0.50	£2.00
1974	365,448,000	£0.10	£0.50	£2.00
1975	197,600,000	£0.10	£0.50	£2.00
1976	412,172,000	£0.10	£0.50	£2.00
1977	86,368,000	£0.10	£0.50	£2.00
1978	59,532,000	£0.10	£0.50	£2.00
1979	219,132,000	£0.10	£0.50	£2.00
1980	202,788,000	£0.10	£0.50	£2.00
1981	46,748,000	£0.10	£0.50	£2.00

TYPE 2 (obverse 1, reverse 2)

		UNC	BU	Proof
1982	190,752,000	£0.05	£0.50	£2.00
1983	7,600,000	£0.50	£2.00	£2.00
1984	158,820 [2]	£2.00	£3.00	£3.00

DOCUMENTED ERRORS
1971 double-headed (mint error) £200

NOTES
[1] Each year, it is determined, based upon supply and demand, what denominations will be struck for circulation. These years were not issued for circulation, and no "business strikes" were made.
[2] These years were not issued for circulation, and the "business strikes" were made for BU mint folders, only.

9

What's currently legal tender?

All 1p coins are legal tender. Merchants are allowed by law to refuse payments made in 1p or 2p coins if the combined total value of the 'coppers' is more than 20p in any one transaction.

Which are hard to find?

The 1972 coin was made as a proof only and went into sets, so is not likely to be found in circulation. In 1992 the Royal Mint changed from using bronze to using copper-plated steel. In that year both types exist and the bronze (non magnetic) 1992 coin is not usually found in circulation.

There is no 'NEW PENNY' error coin relating to one pennies. All 1971 to 1981 coins have 'NEW PENNY' on the reverse and all 1982 to date coins have 'ONE PENNY' on the reverse.... at least they should do! So far no errors have been reported.

OBVERSE

OBVERSE 1
(used 1971 - 1984)
D•G•REG•F•D•(date) || ELIZABETH II
Elizabeth II, Dei Gratia Regina, Fidei Defensor
(Elizabeth II, By the Grace of God Queen and Defender of the Faith)
Portrait by: Arnold Machin

OBVERSE 2
(used 1985 - 1997)
ELIZABETH II || D•G•REG•F•D•(date)
Elizabeth II, Dei Gratia Regina, Fidei Defensor
(Elizabeth II, By the Grace of God Queen and Defender of the Faith)
Portrait by: Raphael Maklouf

OBVERSE 3
(used 1998 - 2008)
ELIZABETH•II•D•G || REG•F•D•(date)
Elizabeth II, Dei Gratia Regina, Fidei Defensor
(Elizabeth II, By the Grace of God Queen and Defender of the Faith)
Portrait by: Ian Rank-Broadley

OBVERSE 4 (similar to last, with no rim beading)
(used 2008 to date)
ELIZABETH•II•D•G || REG•F•D•(date)
Elizabeth II, Dei Gratia Regina, Fidei Defensor
(Elizabeth II, By the Grace of God Queen and Defender of the Faith)
Portrait by: Ian Rank-Broadley

REVERSE

REVERSE 1
(used 1971 - 1981)
Crowned portcullis
[OFFICIALLY: A portcullis with chains royally crowned]
1 NEW PENNY
Design by: Christopher Ironside

REVERSE 2
(used 1982 - 2008)
Crowned portcullis
[OFFICIALLY: A portcullis with chains royally crowned]
1 ONE PENNY
Design by: Christopher Ironside

REVERSE 3
(used 2008 to date)
Lower left section of the Royal coat of Arms of the United Kingdom.
ONE PENNY
Design by: Matthew Dent

TYPE 1 (obverse 1, reverse 1)

		UNC	BU	Proof
1971	1,521,666,250	£0.10	£0.20	£2.00
1972		Proof Only		£5.00
1973	280,196,000	£0.20	£1.00	£3.00
1974	330,892,000	£0.20	£1.00	£3.00
1975	221,604,000	£0.20	£1.00	£3.00
1976	300,160,000	£0.20	£1.00	£3.00
1977	285,430,000	£0.20	£1.00	£3.00
1978	292,770,000	£0.20	£1.00	£2.00
1979	459,000,000	£0.20	£1.00	£2.00
1980	416,304,000	£0.20	£1.00	£2.00
1981	301,800,000	£0.20	£1.00	£2.00

TYPE 2 (obverse 1, reverse 2)

		UNC	BU	Proof
1982	100,292,000	£0.20	£0.70	£2.00
1983	243,002,000	£0.20	£0.70	£2.00
1984	154,759,625	£0.20	£0.70	£2.00

TYPE 3 (obverse 2, reverse 2)

			UNC	BU	Proof
1985	200,605,245		£0.20	£0.70	£2.00
1986	369,989,130		£0.20	£0.70	£2.00
1987	499,946,000		£0.20	£0.70	£2.00
1988	793,492,000		£0.20	£0.70	£2.00
1989	658,142,000		£0.20	£0.70	£2.00
1990	529,047,500		£0.20	£0.70	£2.00
1991	206,457,600		£0.20	£0.70	£2.00
1992	78,421 ‡Al	Bronze	£3.00	£3.00	£3.00

TYPE 4 (obverse 2, reverse 2)
From now on, made of copper-plated steel (which is slightly magnetic)

		UNC	BU	Proof
1992	253,867,000	£0.10	£0.30	-
1993	602,590,000	£0.10	£0.30	£2.00
1994	843,834,000	£0.10	£0.30	£2.00
1995	303,314,000	£0.10	£0.20	£2.00
1996	723,840,060	£0.10	£0.20	£2.00
1997	396,874,000	£0.10	£0.20	£2.00

TYPE 5 (obverse 3, reverse 2)

		UNC	BU	Proof
1998	739,770,000	£0.10	£0.20	£2.00
1999	891,392,000	£0.10	£0.20	£2.00
2000	1,060,364,000	£0.10	£0.20	£2.00
2001	928,802,000	£0.10	£0.20	£2.00
2002	601,446,000	£0.10	£0.20	£2.00
2003	539,436,000	£0.10	£0.20	£2.00
2004	739,764,000	£0.10	£0.20	£2.00
2005	536,318,000	FV	£0.10	£2.00
2006	524,605,000	FV	£0.10	£2.00
2007	548,002,000	FV	£0.10	£2.00
2008	180,600,000	FV	£0.10	£2.00

TYPE 6 (obverse 4 reverse 3)

		UNC	BU	Proof
2008 ‡3	507,952,000	FV	£0.10	£2.00
2009	556,412,800	FV	£0.10	£2.00
2010	609,603,000	FV	£0.10	£2.00
2011	431,004,000	FV	£0.10	£2.00
2012	227,201,000	FV	FV	£2.00
2013	260,800,000	FV	FV	£2.00
2014		FV	FV	£2.00
2015		FV	FV	£2.00

Special Sterling Silver version of TYPE 6

Sterling Silver pennies struck by the Royal Mint and available with pouches, marketed as gifts for new born babies.

			BU
2009	8,467	All prices inc. original packaging	£15.00
2010	9,701		£20.00
2011			£25.00
2012			£25.00
2013			£30.00
2014		Royal Mint, price new	£35.00
2015		Royal Mint, price new	£35.00

NOTES

‡1 These years were not issued for circulation, and no "business strikes" were made.

‡2 These years were not issued for circulation, and the "business strikes" were made for BU mint folders, only.

‡A1 In 1992, a change in materials was made from bronze to copper-plated steel. In 1992 the original bronze planchets were only used for the BU Mint folders and Proof sets. The copper-plated steel planchets were used for circulation strikes only.

‡3 The Dent reverse 2008 1p has been reported to exist with incorrect die alignment.

INFO

Arnold Machin (1911-1999), designed the bust portrait used on decimal coinage, starting in 1968, and used until 1984. It also appeared on the coins of many British Commonwealth nations, including Australia, Canada, and several others. He also designed the reverses of the 1972 Silver Wedding 25p and the 1977 Silver Jubilee 25p. Even with all of this global numismatic exposure, Mr. Machin is probably best known for his portrait used on British postage stamps since 1967, which is estimated to have been printed on over 150 billion stamps.

What's currently legal tender?

All 2p coins are legal tender. Merchants are allowed by law to refuse payments made in 1p or 2p coins if the combined total value of the 'coppers' is more than 20p in any one transaction.

Which are hard to find?

The change from using bronze to using copper-plated steel has led to a couple of scarcer types. The 1992 coin made of bronze (i.e. non magnetic) is much scarcer than the 1992 coin made of copper-plated steel. The same kind of thing happened in 1998, although both types seem common.

By far the rarest and most expensive 2p is the 1983 error coin, which has 'NEW PENCE' on the back instead of 'TWO PENCE'. This mistake just affects the 1983 2p; no other coins have been noted with this error. The error coins went into sets and were not generally circulated. It is possible though, that some of the sets were broken up before the error was noticed, so there may be a few £600 2p coins out there somewhere!

OBVERSE

OBVERSE 1
(used 1971 - 1984)
D•G•REG•F•D•(date) | | ELIZABETH II
Elizabeth II, Dei Gratia Regina, Fidei Defensor
(Elizabeth II, By the Grace of God Queen and Defender of the Faith)
Portrait by: Arnold Machin

OBVERSE 2
(used 1985 - 1997)
ELIZABETH II | | D•G•REG•F•D•(date)
Elizabeth II, Dei Gratia Regina, Fidei Defensor
(Elizabeth II, By the Grace of God Queen and Defender of the Faith)
Portrait by: Raphael Maklouf

OBVERSE 3
(used 1998 - 2008)
ELIZABETH•II•D•G | | REG•F•D•(date)
Elizabeth II, Dei Gratia Regina, Fidei Defensor
(Elizabeth II, By the Grace of God Queen and Defender of the Faith)
Portrait by: Ian Rank-Broadley

OBVERSE 4 (similar to last, with no rim beading)
(used 2008 to date)
ELIZABETH•II•D•G | | REG•F•D•(date)
Elizabeth II, Dei Gratia Regina, Fidei Defensor
(Elizabeth II, By the Grace of God Queen and Defender of the Faith)
Portrait by: Ian Rank-Broadley

REVERSES

REVERSE 1
(used 1971 - 1981)
Plumes in Coronet
[OFFICIALLY: The Badge of the Prince of
Wales, with his motto ICH DIEN]
2 NEW PENCE
Design by: Christopher Ironside

REVERSE 2
(used 1982 - 2008)
Plumes in Coronet
[OFFICIALLY: The Badge of the Prince of
Wales, with his motto ICH DIEN]
2 TWO PENCE
Design by: Christopher Ironside

REVERSE 3
(used 2008 to date)
Upper right section of the Royal coat
of Arms of the United Kingdom.
TWO PENCE
Design by: Matthew Dent

TYPE 1 (obverse 1, reverse 1)

		UNC	BU	Proof
1971	1,454,856,250	£0.10	£0.30	£2.00
1972 Proof Only #1				£4.00
1973 Proof Only #1				£4.00
1974 Proof Only #1				£4.00
1975	145,545,000	£0.20	£0.50	£2.00
1976	181,379,000	£0.20	£0.50	£2.00
1977	109,281,000	£0.20	£0.50	£2.00
1978	189,658,000	£0.20	£0.50	£2.00
1979	260,200,000	£0.20	£0.50	£2.00
1980	408,527,000	£0.20	£0.50	£2.00
1981	353,191,000	£0.20	£0.50	£2.00

TYPE 2 (obverse 1, reverse 2)

		UNC	BU	Proof
1982	205,000 †2	£2.00	£3.00	£3.00
1983	631,000 †2	£2.00	£3.00	£3.00
1983	Error, NEW PENCE reverse £600.00			
1984	158,820 †2	£2.00	£3.00	£3.00

TYPE 3 (obverse 2, reverse 2)

		UNC	BU	Proof
1985	107,113,000	£0.20	£0.50	£2.00
1986	168,967,500	£0.20	£0.50	£2.00
1987	218,100,750	£0.20	£0.50	£2.00
1988	419,889,000	£0.20	£0.50	£2.00
1989	359,226,000	£0.20	£0.50	£2.00
1990	204,499,700	£0.20	£0.50	£2.00
1991	86,625,000	£0.20	£0.50	£2.00
1992	78,421 †B1 Bronze	£3.00	£4.00	£4.00

NOTES

#1	These years were not issued for circulation, and no "business strikes" were made.
†2	These years were not issued for circulation, and the "business strikes" were made for BU mint folders, only.
†B1	In 1992, a change in alloy was made from bronze to copper-plated steel. The original bronze blanks were only used for the BU Mint folders and Proof sets. The copper-plated steel blanks were used for circulation strikes only.
†B2	In 1998, both bronze and copper-plated steel blanks were used. It is estimated that about 55% of the mintage was bronze.
†B3	In 1999, bronze blanks were used for Proof sets.

TYPE 4 (obverse 2, reverse 2) From now on, made of copper-plated steel (slightly magnetic)

			UNC	BU	Proof
1992	102,247,000		£0.10	£0.50	-
1993	235,674,000		£0.10	£0.50	£2.00
1994	531,628,000		£0.10	£0.50	£2.00
1995	124,482,000		£0.10	£0.50	£2.00
1996	296,276,000		£0.10	£0.50	£2.00
1997	496,116,000		£0.10	£0.50	£2.00

TYPE 5 (obverse 3, reverse 2)

1998	231,830,000	Copper/Steel	FV	£0.20	£2.00
1998	About 55% of total +B2	Bronze	FV	£0.20	
1999	353,816,000	Copper/Steel	FV	£0.20	£2.00
1999	+B3	Bronze Proof			£3.00
2000	583,643,000		FV	£0.20	£2.00
2001	551,886,000		FV	£0.20	£2.00
2002	168,556,000		FV	£0.20	£2.00
2003	260,225,000		FV	£0.20	£2.00
2004	356,396,000		FV	£0.20	£2.00
2005	280,396,000		FV	£0.20	£2.00
2006	170,637,000		FV	£0.20	£2.00
2007	254,500,000		FV	£0.20	£2.00
2008	10,600,000				

TYPE 6 (obverse 4, reverse 3)

2008	241,679,000	FV	£0.20	£2.00
2009	150,500,500	FV	£0.20	£2.00
2010	99,600,000	FV	FV	£2.00
2011	114,300,000	FV	FV	£2.00
2012	67,800,000	FV	FV	£2.00
2013	40,600,000	FV	FV	£2.00
2014		FV	FV	£2.00
2015		FV	FV	£2.00

INFO

The current minting facility at Llantrisant, Mid Glamorgan, was built in 1967 in order to meet the demand for the millions of coins needed for the conversion to the modern decimal system used in the United Kingdom.

What's currently legal tender?

Only the smaller post-1990 5p coins are legal tender. The older large coins can be paid into UK bank accounts at face value. The predecessor of the five pence, the shilling, should also be accepted at most UK banks as five pence. Check any shillings have no collectable worth using the Rotographic sister Publication "Collectors' Coins (predecimal issues)" before redeeming them at five pence face value.

Which are hard to find?

The old large 5p coins are no longer found in change (unless someone has managed to pass one off as a 10p, which sometimes happens). The scarcest are those that were made just to go into sets, or as proofs: notably 1972 to 1974, 1976, a few of the early and mid 1980s coins, and the last large 5p struck in 1990.

OBVERSE

OBVERSE 1
(used 1971 - 1984)
D•G•REG•F•D•(date) || ELIZABETH II
Elizabeth II, Dei Gratia Regina, Fidei Defensor
(Elizabeth II, By the Grace of God Queen and Defender of the Faith)
Portrait by: Arnold Machin

OBVERSE 2
(used 1985 - 1990)
ELIZABETH II || D•G•REG•F•D•(date)
Elizabeth II, Dei Gratia Regina, Fidei Defensor
(Elizabeth II, By the Grace of God Queen and Defender of the Faith)
Portrait by: Raphael Maklouf

REVERSE

REVERSE 1
(used 1971 - 1981)
Crowned Thistle
[OFFICIALLY: The Badge of Scotland, a thistle royally crowned]
5 NEW PENCE
Design by: Christopher Ironside

REVERSE 2
(used 1982 - 1990)
Crowned Thistle
[OFFICIALLY: The Badge of Scotland, a thistle royally crowned]
5 FIVE PENCE
Design by: Christopher Ironside

TYPE 1 (obverse 1, reverse 1)

		UNC	BU	Proof
1968	98,868,250	£0.20	£0.40	
1969	120,270,000	£0.20	£1.00	
1970	225,948,525	£0.20	£1.00	
1971	81,783,475	£0.20	£1.00	£2.00
1972	[1]			£5.00
1973	[1]			£5.00
1974	[1]			£5.00
1975	141,539,000	£0.20	£1.00	£2.00
1976	[1]			£4.00
1977	24,308,000	£0.20	£1.00	£2.00
1978	61,094,000	£0.20	£1.00	£2.00
1979	155,456,000	£0.20	£1.00	£2.00
1980	220,566,000	£0.20	£1.00	£2.00
1981	[1]			£4.00

TYPE 2 (obverse 1, reverse 2)

1982	205,000 [2]	£3.00	£4.00	£4.00
1983	631,000 [2]	£3.00	£4.00	£4.00
1984	158,820 [2]	£3.00	£4.00	£4.00

TYPE 3 (obverse 2, reverse 2)

1985	178,000 [2]	£3.00	£4.00	£3.00
1986	167,000 [2]	£3.00	£4.00	£3.00
1987	48,220,000	£0.10	£0.50	£2.00
1988	120,744,610	£0.10	£0.50	£2.00
1989	101,406,000	£0.10	£0.50	£2.00
1990	102,606 [2]	£2.00	£4.00	£4.00

NOTES

[1]   These years were not issued for circulation, and no "business strikes" were made.
[2]   These years were not issued for circulation, and the "business strikes" were made for BU mint folders, only.

18.0 mm • 3.25 grammes • cupro-nickel • milled edge

OBVERSE

OBVERSE 3
(used 1990 - 1997)
ELIZABETH II || D•G•REG•F•D•(date)
Elizabeth II, Dei Gratia Regina, Fidei Defensor
(Elizabeth II, By the Grace of God Queen and Defender of the Faith)
Portrait by: Raphael Maklouf

OBVERSE 4
(used 1998 - 2008)
ELIZABETH II•D•G || REG•F•D•(date)
Elizabeth II, Dei Gratia Regina, Fidei Defensor
(Elizabeth II, By the Grace of God Queen and Defender of the Faith)
Portrait by: Ian Rank-Broadley

OBVERSE 5 (similar to last, with no rim beading)
(used 2008 to date)
ELIZABETH II•D•G || REG•F•D•(date)
Elizabeth II, Dei Gratia Regina, Fidei Defensor
(Elizabeth II, By the Grace of God Queen and Defender of the Faith)
Portrait by: Ian Rank-Broadley

REVERSE

REVERSE 3
(used 1990 - 2008)
Crowned Thistle
[OFFICIALLY: The Badge of Scotland, a thistle royally crowned]
5 FIVE PENCE
Design by: Christopher Ironside

REVERSE 4
(used 2008 to date)
Middle part of the Royal coat of Arms of the United Kingdom.
FIVE PENCE
Design by: Matthew Dent

INFO

As of December 31st 1990, the large
five-pence coins were demonetised.

TYPE 4 (obverse 3, reverse 3)

		UNC	BU	Proof
1990	1,634,976,005 ‡3	£0.10	£0.30	£2.00
1991	724,979,000	£0.10	£0.30	£2.00
1992	453,173,500	£0.10	£0.30	£2.00
1993	56,945 ‡2	£2.00	£3.00	£3.00
1994	93,602,000	£0.10	£0.30	£2.00
1995	183,384,000	£0.10	£0.30	£2.00
1996	302,902,000	£0.10	£0.30	£2.00
1997	236,596,000	£0.10	£0.30	£2.00

TYPE 5 (obverse 4, reverse 3)

1998	217,376,000	100,000 proofs	FV	£0.30	£2.00
1999	195,490,000		FV	£0.30	£2.00
2000	388,506,000		FV	£0.30	£2.00
2001	320,330,000		FV	£0.30	£2.00
2002	219,258,000		FV	£0.30	£2.00
2003	333,230,000		FV	£0.30	£2.00
2004	271,810,000		FV	£0.30	£2.00
2005	236,212,000		FV	£0.20	£2.00
2006	317,697,000		FV	£0.20	£2.00
2007	246,720,000		FV	£0.20	£2.00
2008	92,880,000		FV	£0.20	£2.00

TYPE 6 (obverse 5, reverse 4)

2008 ‡4	165,172,000		FV	£0.20	£2.00
2009	132,960,300		FV	£0.20	£2.00
2010	396,245,500		FV	FV	£2.00
2011	50,400,000		FV	FV	£2.00
2012	339,802,350	Nickel plated steel	FV	FV	£2.00
2013	378,800,750	Nickel plated steel	FV	FV	£2.00
2014		Nickel plated steel	FV	FV	£2.00
2015		Nickel plated steel	FV	FV	£2.00

NOTES

‡2   1993 was not issued for circulation, and the "business strikes" were made for BU mint folders, only.

‡3   A 1990 Silver proof set with both large and small type coins was issued. Value approx £25

‡4   The Dent reverse 2008 5p has been reported to exist with incorrect die alignment of up to 180 degrees!

21

What's currently legal tender?

Only the smaller post-1992 10p coins are legal tender. The older large coins can be paid into UK bank accounts. The predecessor of the ten pence, the florin or two-shillings, should also be accepted at most UK banks. Check any florins have no collectable worth using the Rotographic sister publication "Collectors' Coins" before redeeming them at ten pence face value.

Which are hard to find?

The old large 10p coins are no longer found in change. The scarcest are those that were made just to go into sets, or as proofs: notably 1972, 1978 and all of the large type coins from 1982 onwards. There are lots of known varieties for the Ten Pence, both larger size and current size. See the end of this section.

OBVERSE

OBVERSE 1
(used 1971 - 1984)
D•G•REG•F•D•(date) || ELIZABETH II
Elizabeth II, Dei Gratia Regina, Fidei Defensor
(Elizabeth II, By the Grace of God Queen and Defender of the Faith)
Portrait by: Arnold Machin

OBVERSE 2
(used 1985 - 1992)
ELIZABETH II || D•G•REG•F•D•(date)
Elizabeth II, Dei Gratia Regina, Fidei Defensor
(Elizabeth II, By the Grace of God Queen and Defender of the Faith)
Portrait by: Raphael Maklouf

REVERSE

REVERSE 1
(used 1971 - 1981)
Lion Passant Guardant
[Part of the crest of England, a lion passant guardant royally crowned]
10 NEW PENCE
Design by: Christopher Ironside

REVERSE 2
(used 1982 - 1992)
Lion Passant Guardant
[Part of the crest of England, a lion passant guardant royally crowned]
10 TEN PENCE
Design by: Christopher Ironside

TYPE 1 (obverse 1, reverse 1)

			UNC	BU	Proof
1968	336,143,250		£0.20	£0.50	
1969	314,008,000		£0.20	£0.50	
1970	133,571,000		£0.20	£1.00	
1971	63,205,000		£0.20	£1.00	£2.00
1972	[1]	Proof Only			£5.00
1973	152,174,000		£0.20	£1.00	£2.00
1974	92,741,000		£0.20	£1.00	£2.00
1975	181,559,000		£0.20	£1.00	£2.00
1976	228,220,000		£0.20	£1.00	£2.00
1977	59,323,000		£0.20	£1.00	£2.00
1978	[1]	Proof Only			£5.00
1979	115,457,000		£0.20	£1.00	£2.00
1980	88,650,000		£0.40	£1.00	£2.00
1981	3,487,000		£1.00	£4.00	£5.00

TYPE 2 (obverse 1, reverse 2)

			UNC	BU	Proof
1982	205,000 [2]		£3.00	£4.00	£4.00
1983	631,000 [2]		£3.00	£4.00	£4.00
1984	158,820 [2]		£3.00	£4.00	£4.00

TYPE 3 (obverse 2, reverse 2)

			UNC	BU	Proof
1985	178,000 [2]		£3.00	£4.00	£4.00
1986	167,000 [2]		£3.00	£4.00	£4.00
1987	172,425 [2]		£3.00	£4.00	£4.00
1988	134,067 [2]		£3.00	£4.00	£4.00
1989	77,569 [2]		£3.00	£4.00	£4.00
1990	102,606 [2]		£2.00	£4.00	£4.00
1991	74,975 [2]		£2.00	£4.00	£4.00
1992	78,421 [2]		£2.00	£4.00	£4.00

NOTES

[1]   These years were not issued for circulation, and no "business strikes" were made.

[2]   These years were not issued for circulation, and the "business strikes" were made for BU mint folders, only.

INFO

As of 30th June 1993, the large ten-pence coins were demonetised.

23

OBVERSE

OBVERSE 3
(used 1992 - 1997)
ELIZABETH II || D•G•REG•F•D•(date)
Elizabeth II, Dei Gratia Regina, Fidei Defensor
(Elizabeth II, By the Grace of God Queen and Defender of the Faith)
Portrait by: Raphael Maklouf

OBVERSE 4
(used 1998 - 2008)
ELIZABETH II•D•G || REG•F•D•(date)
Elizabeth II, Dei Gratia Regina, Fidei Defensor
(Elizabeth II, By the Grace of God Queen and Defender of the Faith)
Portrait by: Ian Rank-Broadley

OBVERSE 5 (similar to last, with no rim beading)
(used 2008 to date)
ELIZABETH II•D•G || REG•F•D•(date)
Elizabeth II, Dei Gratia Regina, Fidei Defensor
(Elizabeth II, By the Grace of God Queen and Defender of the Faith)
Portrait by: Ian Rank-Broadley

REVERSE

REVERSE 3
(used 1992 - 2008)
Lion Passant Guardant
[Part of the crest of England, a lion passant guardant royally crowned]
10 TEN PENCE
Design by: Christopher Ironside

REVERSE 4
(used 2008 to date)
Upper left section of the Royal coat of Arms of the
United Kingdom.
10 TEN PENCE
Design by: Matthew Dent

TYPE 4 (obverse 3, reverse 3)

		UNC	BU	Proof
1992	1,413,455,170	£0.15	£0.50	£2.00
1993	‡Cl	£0.15	£0.50	£2.00
1994	56,945 ‡2	£1.00	£4.00	£4.00
1995	43,259,000	£0.15	£0.50	£2.00
1996	118,738,000	£0.15	£0.50	£2.00
1997	99,196,000	£0.15	£0.50	£2.00

TYPE 5 (obverse 4, reverse 3)

		UNC	BU	Proof
1998	‡2 100,000 proofs	£2.00	£4.00	£4.00
1999	‡2	£2.00	£4.00	£4.00
2000	134,727,000	£0.20	£0.30	£2.00
2001	82,081,000	£0.20	£0.30	£2.00
2002	80,934,000	£0.20	£0.30	£2.00
2003	88,118,000	£0.20	£0.30	£2.00
2004	99,602,000	FV	£0.30	£2.00
2005	69,604,000 ‡Cl '1' of '10' to bead or space	FV	£0.30	£2.00
2006	118,803,000 ‡Cl	FV	£0.30	£2.00
2007	72,720,000	FV	£0.30	£2.00
2008	9,720,000	FV	£0.30	£2.00

TYPE 6 (obverse 5, reverse 4)

			UNC	BU	Proof
2008	71,447,000		FV	FV	£2.00
2009	84,360,000		FV	FV	£2.00
2010	96,600,500		FV	FV	£2.00
2011	59,603,850		FV	FV	£2.00
2012	11,600,030	Nickel plated steel	FV	FV	£2.00
2013	320,200,750	Nickel plated steel	FV	FV	£2.00
2014		Nickel plated steel	FV	FV	£2.00
2015		Nickel plated steel	FV	FV	£2.00

NOTES

‡2   These years were not issued for circulation, and the "business strikes" were made for BU mint folders, only.

‡Cl   Varieties exist for the 1992 issue, see next pages Reverses 1 & 2 listed below have also been observed on 2005 and 2006 dated coins. It is not yet clear if one type is scarcer than the other.

25

TEN PENCE VARIETIES - Early, large size coins

There are a large number of subtle die varieties known for the Ten pences struck from the earliest in 1968, right through to the 1980s. The varieties first came to light in the 1970s, surveyed (among others) by Ron Stafford, who published a few incredibly detailed articles on them. The majority of the varieties concern the number of beads in the borders and the precise positioning of the letters and numbers, in relation to the border beads. It can make your eyes go funny just reading about it!

While significant, I feel that due to the complex nature, space required to list them all and the fact that the varieties are not often differentiated between, that it would perhaps be a better idea to mention them here, but not go in to any detail.

TEN PENCE VARIETIES - Later, smaller coins

The production of the new 1992 smaller sized ten pence piece has yielded several varieties, some of which appear to be much less common than others.

The first type of ten pence pieces have a "wired" edge (left coin in both images), which has a curved edge, while all other varieties have a "flat" sharper edge (right coin in both images).

Obverse 1: The letters L and I in ELIZABETH point between 2 border beads. Obverse 2: The letters L and I in ELIZABETH point directly at border beads.

Reverse 1: The number 1 in the "10" points directly at a border bead. Reverse 2: The number 1 in the "10" points between 2 border beads.

TEN PENCE VARIETIES - Later, smaller coins

1992 Ten Pence types:

TYPE 1: wired edge, obverse 1 reverse 1
Earliest type. It appears that the "wired" edge was abandoned sometime around midway through 1992 production. Represents approximately 40% of total mintage.

TYPE 2: flat edge, obverse 1 reverse 1
A continuation of the TYPE 1, but on different planchets with flat edges. This type also represents approximately 40% of the total mintage.

TYPE 3: flat edge, obverse 1 reverse 2
An extremely uncommon variety, referred to as the "between/between" type. Represents about 3% of the total mintage, perhaps a little less. This type could become desirable in the future.

TYPE 4: flat edge, obverse 2 reverse 1
The rarest variety, referred to as the "to dot/to dot" variety. Represents less than 1% of the total mintage, with some estimates as low as one half of 1%. This type may be worth saving for the future.

TYPE 5: flat edge, obverse 2 reverse 2
This type exhibits a new obverse and reverse style. Represents approximately 15% of the total mintage. This is the type is found in Proof sets and BU Mint folders.

From 1993 to 2006 it seems that the circulation coins all have Reverse 1 (i.e the '1' of '10' pointing directly at a border bead) and that proof coins and coins in the BU sets have Reverse 2 (the '1' of '10' pointing between two border beads). It is not known 100% if this trend continued up to 2008 (the last year of the old reverse design).

What's currently legal tender?

All 20p coins are legal tender. Victorian Double Florins also appear to be legal tender for 20p (4 shillings) as the author is unable to find any evidence that they were demonetised in 1971 with the rest of the old denominations. To spend one would be quite silly though, as the value of the silver contained within a double florin is far higher than 20p!

Which are hard to find?

The 1986 20p was made to be put in sets only and is therefore incredibly hard to find in change.

The new design 20p with no date is scarce. This coin is technically known as a mule and occured because the Royal Mint used the old obverse (OBVERSE 3) with the new reverse (REVERSE 2) in error, resulting in a coin with no date on it. All the errors should have been dated 2008 as the Royal Mint noticed the error after about 100,000 of the first coins were struck.

I get contacted a lot by people that have found one of these, hoping that they are worth £400+, as they were indeed selling for that much after the incredible amount of hype when the media first picked up the story and the public speculated. Collectors had known about them for months but the whole thing was blown massively out of proportion!

The approximate mintage number of the mule 20p claimed by the Royal Mint of 100,000+ would seem to be supported by the quite large volume of these offered for sale. Clearly this is a very low number of coins compared to all of the other 20p annual mintages! But 100,000 cannot really be deemed as rare. 1000 would be scarce. 100 would be quite rare. It should be borne in mind though, that rarity alone doesn't always lead to high values. High demand and not-enough-to-go-round is what causes things to be expensive. This is exactly what happened - all of a sudden thousands of people that wouldn't normally do anything with coins, apart from spend them, all wanted an error 20p!

Back to that low mintage number of about 100,000 - assuming that number is about right, it makes them approximately as scarce as the 1951 British penny. In the 1960s a similar thing happened (a little slower of course, because many people didn't even have televisions and the chap that invented the internet was still in short trousers) and the prices of known scarce coins were artificially inflated by people speculating that they would be a good idea to save for a rainy day. 50-odd years later and an absolutely perfect shimmering BU 1951 penny is worth less than £100 (in real terms, less than what people were paying for them in the 1960s). I could be wrong, but I suspect the same will be true of the mule 20p in 60 years time. They will remain collectable, but the demand will never again outstrip the supply and as a result the values will stay at a more realistic level.

I also predict that in the future the near perfect examples removed from circulation early on will be more sought after than the majority of the coins that were taken from circulation at the point of maximum hype after being used and abused for 6+ months. The 20p is a popular coin and many that I saw for sale were far from perfect even after minimal circulation. Collectors are very fussy and always prefer the very best quality.

OBVERSE

OBVERSE 1
(used 1982 - 1984)
ELIZABETH II | | D•G•REG•F•D
Elizabeth II, Dei Gratia Regina, Fidei Defensor
(Elizabeth II, By the Grace of God Queen and Defender of the Faith)
Portrait by: Arnold Machin

OBVERSE 2
(used 1985 - 1997, with a slight change in 1992)
ELIZABETH II | | D•G•REG•F•D
Elizabeth II, Dei Gratia Regina, Fidei Defensor
(Elizabeth II, By the Grace of God Queen and Defender of the Faith)
Portrait by: Raphael Maklouf

OBVERSE 3
(used 1998 - 2008)
ELIZABETH II | | D•G•REG•F•D
Elizabeth II, Dei Gratia Regina, Fidei Defensor
(Elizabeth II, By the Grace of God Queen and Defender of the Faith)
Portrait by: Ian Rank-Broadley

OBVERSE 4
(used 2008 to date)
ELIZABETH•II•D•G•REG•F•D•(date)
Elizabeth II, Dei Gratia Regina, Fidei Defensor
(Elizabeth II, By the Grace of God Queen and Defender of the Faith)
Portrait by: Ian Rank-Broadley

REVERSE

REVERSE 1
(used 1982 - 2008)
Crowned Tudor Rose
[The Badge of England, a royally crowned double rose]
20 TWENTY PENCE (date)
Design by: William Gardner

REVERSE 2
(used 2008 to date)
Lower right section of the Royal coat of Arms of the
United Kingdom.
TWENTY PENCE
Design by: Matthew Dent

21.40 mm • 5.00 grammes • cupro-nickel • plain edge

TYPE 1 (obverse 1, reverse 1)

		UNC	BU	Proof
1982	740,815,000	£0.30	£0.50	£2.00
	Specimen in folder		£2.00	
	Silver piedfort proof			£20.00
1983	158,463,000	£0.30	£0.50	£2.00
1984	65,350,965	£0.30	£0.50	£2.00

TYPE 2 (obverse 2, reverse 1)

			UNC	BU	Proof
1985	74,273,699		£0.30	£0.50	£2.00
1986	167,000 ‡2		£4.00	£5.00	£5.00
1987	137,450,000		£0.30	£0.50	£2.00
1988	38,038,344		£0.30	£0.50	£2.00
1989	132,013,890		£0.30	£0.50	£2.00
1990	88,097,500		£0.30	£0.50	£2.00
1991	35,901,250		£0.30	£0.50	£2.00
1992	31,205,000 (both)	Small head*	£0.50	£1.00	£5.00
1992		Large head*	£1.00	£2.00	exists?
1993	123,123,750		£0.30	£0.50	£3.00
1994	67,131,250		£0.30	£0.50	£3.00
1995	102,005,000		£0.30	£0.50	£3.00
1996	83,163,750		£0.30	£0.50	£3.00
1997	89,518,750		£0.30	£0.50	£3.00

TYPE 3 (obverse 3, reverse 1)

		UNC	BU	Proof
1998	76,965,000	FV	£0.50	£3.00
1999	73,478,750	FV	£0.50	£3.00
2000	136,418,750	FV	£0.50	£2.00
2001	148,122,500	FV	£0.50	£2.00
2002	93,360,000	FV	£0.50	£2.00
2003	153,383,750	FV	£0.50	£2.00
2004	120,212,500	FV	£0.50	£2.00
2005	154,488,750	FV	£0.50	£2.00
2006	114,800,000	FV	£0.50	£2.00
2007	117,075,000	FV	£0.50	£2.00
2008	11,900,000	FV	£0.50	£2.00

* The 1992 small head coin was thought to be scarcer than the large head, but new information would seem to imply that the large head coins are the coins that were circulated in large numbers and are now hardest to find (especially in top condition as most have seen normal usage). It is now thought that the proof version only exists with the small head. The easiest way to tell the difference is that the small head bust has a much sharper point where the neck ends at the bottom.
The obverse 2 picture on the previous page is the smaller 'sharp neck' type.

MULE ERROR (mis-matching obverse 3 and reverse 2)

	UNC	BU	Proof
(2008) Also known as the 'dateless' 20p <u>Used, up to: £30</u>	£50	£75	-

Chinese made fakes exist. They have a dirty matt appearance, thinner lettering and a lack of detail.

TYPE 4 (obverse 4, reverse 2)

		UNC	BU	Proof
2008 [3]	115,022,000	FV	£0.30	£2.00
2009	121,625,300	FV	£0.30	£2.00
2010	112,875,500	FV	£0.30	£2.00
2011	191,625,000	FV	FV	£2.00
2012	69,650,030	FV	FV	£2.00
2013	66,325,000	FV	FV	£2.00
2014		FV	FV	£2.00
2015		FV	FV	£2.00

NOTES

[2]   Each year, it is determined, based upon supply and demand, what denominations will be struck for circulation. 1986 was not issued for circulation, and the "business strikes" were made for BU mint folders, only.

[3]   The 2008 new design (non mule) coin and also some 2009 coins exist with what was originally thought to be a small raised 'I' on the reverse. It is probably actually a die crack, rather than any deliberate mint identification. Interesting nonetheless, as a few of these are known to exist. This same 'I' die crack coin has also been reported dated 2010, but is yet to be confirmed.

2008 20p reverse with small 'I'.

Historically the Crown is five shillings (one quarter of a 20 shilling pound). Therefore the new decimal crowns had a face value of 25p. These four commemorative crown coins are legal tender for 25p, but they are rarely used by the public, probably because they are too big to be convenient, and to collectors they are usually worth a little more than face value. Members of the public often assume incorrectly that these four coins have a face value of £5, due to the fact that the crown was re-valued to £5 in 1990 although the size of the coin remained the same.

For later Crowns, see the FIVE POUNDS section.

These four coins were issued to mark the following occasions: 1972 – The 25th Wedding Anniversary of the Queen and Prince Philip. 1977 - The Silver Jubilee of the Queen. 1980 - The 80th Birthday of the Queen Mother. 1981 - The Royal Wedding of Charles and Diana.

COMMEMORATIVE TYPE 1
Obverse: Standard portrait of QE II
Design by: Arnold Machin

Reverse: Elizabeth and Philip,
20 November 1947-1972
Design by: Arnold Machin

		UNC	BU	Proof
1972	7,452,100	£1.00	£1.50	£4.00
	100,000	.925 sterling silver proof		£20.00

COMMEMORATIVE TYPE 2
Obverse: Equestrian portrait of QE II
Design by: Arnold Machin

Reverse: Ampulla and anointing spoon,
items used during the Coronation
Design by: Arnold Machin

			UNC	BU	Proof
1977	37,061,160		£0.50	£1.00	£4.00
	Specimen in folder			£1.00	
	377,000	.925 sterling silver proof			£15.00

COMMEMORATIVE TYPE 3
Obverse: Standard portrait of QE II
Design by: Arnold Machin

Reverse: Portrait of Queen Mother,
surrounded by bows and lions
Design by: Richard Guyatt

1980	9,306,000	-	£1.00	£2.00	-
	Specimen in folder			£2.00	
	83,672	.925 sterling silver proof			£20.00

COMMEMORATIVE TYPE 4
Obverse: Standard portrait of QE II
Design by: Arnold Machin

Reverse: Conjoined busts of
Charles & Diana
Design by: Philip Nathan

1981	26,773,600	-	£1.00	£2.00	-
	Specimen in folder			£2.00	
	218,000	.925 sterling silver proof			£20.00

Set of 4 (72, 77, 80 and 81) Crowns as silver proofs in large case. 5000 sets issued £65.00

33

What's currently legal tender?

Only the smaller (post-1997) 50p coins are legal tender now. Most banks will allow you to pay in used pre-1997 larger 30mm coins.

Which are hard to find?

The most significant 50p that could possibly be found in change is the withdrawn Olympic Aquatics coin with the lines on the swimmers' face. See Commemorative Type 17. The prices for the Kew Gardens 2009 50p are also quite high, following media exposure when it was discovered that this particular coin has the lowest mintage of all the circulating 50p coins. The 1992-1993 EU coin is also experiencing higher prices.

In 2009 a complete set of coins featuring all the sixteen 1969 - 2009 designs was issued as cupro-nickel proof and sterling silver proof sets. All of them are the newer 27.3mm size and all feature the Ian Rank-Broadley portrait of the Queen (OBVERSE 4). See after commemorative type 5.

OBVERSE

OBVERSE 1
(used 1969 - 1972, 1974 - 1984)
D•G•REG•F•D•(date) || ELIZABETH II
Elizabeth II, Dei Gratia Regina, Fidei Defensor
(Elizabeth II, By the Grace of God Queen and Defender of the Faith)
Portrait by: Arnold Machin

OBVERSE 2
(used 1985 - 1997)
ELIZABETH II || D•G•REG•F•D•(date)
Elizabeth II, Dei Gratia Regina, Fidei Defensor
(Elizabeth II, By the Grace of God Queen and Defender of the Faith)
Portrait by: Raphael Maklouf

REVERSE

REVERSE 1 (left)
(used 1969 - 1972, 1974 - 1981)
Britannia
[The seated figure of Britannia]
50 NEW PENCE
Design by: Christopher Ironside

REVERSE 2 (right)
(used 1982 - 93, 1995 - 1997)
Britannia
[The seated figure of Britannia]
50 FIFTY PENCE
Design by: Christopher Ironside

34

Britannia - TYPE 1 (obverse 1, reverse 1)

		UNC	BU	Proof
1969	188,400,000	£1.00	£2.00	
1970	19,461,500	£1.00	£4.00	
1971	‡1	Proof Only		£5.00
1972	‡1	Proof Only		£5.00
1974	‡1	Proof Only		£5.00
1975	‡1	Proof Only		£5.00
1976	43,746,500	£1.00	£3.00	£4.00
1977	49,536,000	£1.00	£3.00	£4.00
1978	72,005,500	£1.00	£3.00	£4.00
1979	58,680,000	£1.00	£3.00	£4.00
1980	89,086,000	£1.00	£3.00	£4.00
1981	74,002,000	£1.00	£3.00	£4.00

Britannia - TYPE 2 (obverse 1, reverse 2)

		UNC	BU	Proof
1982	51,312,000	£1.00	£3.00	£4.00
1983	62,824,904	£1.00	£3.00	£4.00
1984	158,820 ‡2	£2.00	£5.00	£5.00

Britannia - TYPE 3 (obverse 2, reverse 2)

		UNC	BU	Proof
1985	682,103	£2.00	£4.00	£5.00
1986	167,000 ‡2	£3.00	£5.00	£5.00
1987	172,425 ‡2	£3.00	£5.00	£5.00
1988	134,067 ‡2	£3.00	£5.00	£5.00
1989	77,569 ‡2	£3.00	£5.00	£5.00
1990	102,606 ‡2	£3.00	£5.00	£5.00
1991	74,975 ‡2	£3.00	£5.00	£5.00
1992	78,421 ‡2	£3.00	£5.00	£5.00
1993	56,945 ‡2	£3.00	£5.00	£5.00
1994	Marked 'ROYAL MINT TRIAL'		£600.00*	
1995	105,647 ‡2	£3.00	£5.00	£5.00
1996	86,501 ‡2	£3.00	£5.00	£5.00
1997	‡2	£3.00	£5.00	£5.00

NOTES

‡1   These years were not issued for circulation, and no "business strikes" were made.

‡2   These years were not issued for circulation, and the "business strikes" were made for BU mint folders, only.

*   Extremely rare 1994 'ROYAL MINT TRIAL' coins exist. The standard design is used. One known trial is round, not 7-sided. Not to be confused with commemorative type 3, which is also dated 1994!

27.3 mm • 8.0 grammes • cupro-nickel • plain edge

OBVERSE

OBVERSE 3
(used 1997)
ELIZABETH II || D•G•REG•F•D•(date)
Elizabeth II, Dei Gratia Regina, Fidei Defensor
(Elizabeth II, By the Grace of God Queen and Defender of the Faith)
Portrait by: Raphael Maklouf

OBVERSE 4
(used 1998 - 2008 and for some commemorative Fifty Pences)
ELIZABETH II || D•G•REG•F•D•(date)
Elizabeth II, Dei Gratia Regina, Fidei Defensor
(Elizabeth II, By the Grace of God Queen and Defender of the Faith)
Portrait by: Ian Rank-Broadley

OBVERSE 5 (similar to last, with different alignment)
(used 2008 to date with Reverse 4)
ELIZABETH II || D•G•REG•F•D•(date)
Elizabeth II, Dei Gratia Regina, Fidei Defensor
(Elizabeth II, By the Grace of God Queen and Defender of the Faith)
Portrait by: Ian Rank-Broadley

REVERSE

REVERSE 3
(used 1997 - 2008)
Often referred to as the 'Britannia issue' to distinguish it from the
commemorative issues.
[The seated figure of Britannia]
50 FIFTY PENCE
Design by: Christopher Ironside

REVERSE 4
(used 2008 to date)
Bottom section of the Royal coat of Arms of the
United Kingdom.
FIFTY PENCE
Design by: Matthew Dent

Britannia - TYPE 4 (obverse 3, reverse 3)

		UNC	BU	Proof
1997	456,364,100	£1.00	£2.00	

Britannia - TYPE 5 (obverse 4, reverse 3)

1998	64,306,500	£1.00	£2.00	
1999	24,905,000	£1.00	£2.00	£3.00
2000	27,915,500	£1.00	£2.00	£3.00
2001	84,998,500	£1.00	£2.00	£3.00
2002	23,907,500	£1.00	£2.00	£3.00
2003	23,583,000	£1.00	£2.00	£3.00
2004	35,315,500	£1.00	£2.00	£3.00
2005	30,354,500	£1.00	£2.00	£3.00
2006	24,567,000	£1.00	£2.00	£3.00
2007	11,200,000	£1.00	£2.00	£3.00
2008	3,500,000	£1.00	£2.00	£3.00

New non-commemerative - TYPE 6 (obverse 5, reverse 4)

2008	22,747,000		FV	£1.00	£3.00
2009	None for circulation	(106,332 in sets)		£3.00	£4.00
2010	None for circulation	(69,189 in sets)		£4.00	£4.00
2011	None for circulation	(56,007 in sets)		£5.00	£4.00
2012	32,300,030		FV	FV	£3.00
2013	10,301,000		FV	FV	£3.00
2014			FV	FV	£3.00
2015			FV	FV	£3.00

DOCUMENTED ERRORS
1969 double-headed (minting error) £150+
19?? undated "double-tailed" (minting error) £200+

INFO
The "straight" edges of the 50p (and the 20p) are not flat, but arced to form a Reuleaux polygon. Any point on an arced edge is an equal distance from the opposing vertex. This design enables the coins to be used in vending machines.

37

| 30 mm • 13.5 grammes • cupro-nickel • plain edge |

COMMEMORATIVE TYPE 1
1973 || 50 || pence (centre)
Nine clasped hands forming a circle
(Britain's entry into the European
Economic Community)
Reverse design by: David Wynne
(also exists dated 2009, see page 39)

		UNC	BU	Proof
1973	89,775,000	£1.00	£2.00	£4.00
	Proof in leatherette case			£4.00
	thick planchet but not recorded as Piedfort			?

COMMEMORATIVE TYPE 2
1992-1993 (upper) || 50 pence (lower)
Conference table with seats and stars
(completion of the EC single market and
the British Presidency)
Reverse design by: Mary Milner Dickens
(also exists dated 2009, see page 39)

		Used	UNC/BU	Proof
1992-1993	109,000	£10?*	£30/£40	£40
	Specimen in folder (including Britannia issue)		£35	
	26,890 .925 sterling silver proof			£40
	15,000 .925 sterling silver piedfort proof			£50
	1,864 .917 gold proof			£600

Since being reported as the old size 50p with the lowest mintage, interest and prices have increased.
Used examples aren't encountered that often.

COMMEMORATIVE TYPE 3
50 pence (lower right)
**Ships and planes taking part in the
D-Day landings**
(50th Anniversary of the D-Day Invasion)
Reverse design by: John Mills
(also exists dated 2009, see page 39)

		UNC	BU	Proof
1994	6.705,520	£1.00	£2.00	£4.00
	Specimen in folder		£2.00	
	40,500 .925 sterling silver proof			£24.00
	10,000 .925 sterling silver piedfort proof			£30.00
	1,877 .917 gold proof			£600.00

COMMEMORATIVE TYPE 4
1973 EU 1998 || 50 pence (lower)
Fireworks pattern of 12 stars
(25th Anniversary - UK entry into EEC)
Design by: John Mills
(also exists dated 2009, see below)

		UNC	BU	Proof
1998	5,043,000	£1.00	£2.00	£5.00
	Specimen in folder (including Britannia issue)		£7.00	
8,854	.925 sterling silver proof			£30.00
5,117	.925 sterling silver piedfort proof			£40.00
1,177	.917 gold proof			£450.00

COMMEMORATIVE TYPE 5
FIFTIETH ANNIVERSARY (upper) || 50 pence (lower)
Caring Hands, holding sun's rays
(50th Annirversary - National Health Service)
Design by: Mary Milner Dickens
(also exists dated 2009, see below)

		UNC	BU	Proof
1998	5,001,000	£1.00	£2.00	£5.00
	Specimen in folder		£3.00	
9,029	.925 sterling silver proof			£20.00
5,117	.925 sterling silver piedfort proof			£30.00
651	.917 gold proof			£450.00

The 2009 retrospective 40th Anniversary set of sixteen fifty pence coins.

From the introduction of the 50p in 1969 up to and including the 2009 Kew Gardens coin there were a total of 16 different 50p reverses used. These large types:

Standard Britannia with 'NEW PENCE' (REVERSE 1)
EEC Hands (commemorative TYPE 1)
Standard Britannia with 'FIFTY PENCE' (REVERSE 2)
EC 1992-1993 (commemorative TYPE 2)
D-Day (commemorative TYPE 3)

Followed by the smaller commemorative types 4 to 13 and the REVERSE 4 of the normal 50p.

All of these designs were sold in sets of 16, all featuring OBVERSE 4 and all being of the newer 27.3mm diameter, even the five listed above that were originally larger. Only just over 1000 of each cupro-nickel or silver set were made and they are both hard to find. Values? £250+ perhaps?

Very rare: There were also 70 gold proof sets and 40 gold proof piedfort sets made!

39

27.3 mm • 8.0 grammes • cupro-nickel • plain edge

1850-2000 (upper) || PUBLIC LIBRARIES (lower)
Open book upon pillared building
(150th Anniversary - British Libraries)
Design by: Mary Milner Dickens
(also exists dated 2009, see page 39)

			UNC	BU	Proof
2000	11,263,000		£1.00	£3.00	£5.00
		Specimen in folder		£4.00	
		.925 sterling silver proof			£20.00
	5,721	.925 sterling silver piedfort proof			£30.00
	710	.917 gold proof			£475.00

50 pence (left) || 1903-2003 (lower right)
Suffragette with WSPU banner
(100th Anniversary - Women's Social and Political Union)
Design by: Mary Milner Dickens
(also exists dated 2009, see page 39)

			UNC	BU	Proof
2003	3,124,030	(43,513 proofs in sets)	£1.00	£3.00	£5.00
	9,582	Specimen in folder		£4.00	
	6,267 of 15k	.925 sterling silver proof			£20.00
	6,795 of 7.5k	.925 sterling silver piedfort proof			£30.00
	942 of 1000	.917 gold proof			£475.00

50 pence (lower)
Runner's legs and stopwatch
(50th Anniversary - Roger Bannister's 4-minute mile run)
Design by: James Butler
(also exists dated 2009, see page 39)

			UNC	BU	Proof
2004	9,032,500	(35,020 proofs in sets)	£0.80	£3.00	£5.00
	10,371	Specimen in folder		£4.00	
	4,924 of 15k	.925 sterling silver proof			£20.00
	4,054 of 7.5k	.925 sterling silver piedfort proof			£30.00
	644 of 1,250	.917 gold proof			£475.00

COMMEMORATIVE TYPE 9
50 (upper) || JOHNSON'S DICTIONARY 1755 (lower)
Dictionary entries for Fifty and Pence
(250th Anniversary - Samuel Johnson's English Dictionary)
Design by: Tom Phillips
(also exists dated 2009, see page 39)

			UNC	BU	Proof
2005	17,649,000	(40,563 proofs in sets) £1.00		£2.00	£5.00
		Specimen in folder		£3.00	
	4,029 of 7,500	.925 sterling silver proof			£20.00
	3,808 of 5,000	.925 sterling silver piedfort proof			£30.00
	1,000	.917 gold proof			£475.00

COMMEMORATIVE TYPE 10
FIFTY PENCE (lower)
Representation of the heroic acts performed by VC recipients
(150th Anniversary - Institution of the Victoria Cross)
Design by: Clive Duncan
(also exists dated 2009, see page 39)

			UNC	BU	Proof
2006	10,000,500	(37,689 proofs in sets) £1.00		£2.00	£5.00
	31,266	Specimen in folder		£5.00	
	6,872 of 7,500	.925 sterling silver proof			£20.00
	3,415 of 5,000	.925 sterling silver piedfort proof			£40.00
	804 of 1000	.917 gold proof			£475.00

COMMEMORATIVE TYPE 11
VC || FIFTY PENCE
The obverse and reverse of the Victoria Cross
(150th Anniversary - Institution of the Victoria Cross)
Design by: Claire Aldridge
(also exists dated 2009, see page 39)

			UNC	BU	Proof
2006	12,087,000	(37,689 proofs in sets) £1.00		£2.00	£5.00
	37,176	Specimen in folder		£3.00	
	6,310 of 7,500	.925 sterling silver proof			£20.00
	3,532 of 5,000	.925 sterling silver piedfort proof			£30.00
	866 of 1000	.917 gold proof			£475.00

27.3 mm • 8.0 grammes • cupro-nickel • plain edge

COMMEMORATIVE TYPE 12
FIFTY PENCE | 1907 | BE PREPARED | 2007
The scouting badge
(100th Anniversary - The Scout Movement)
Design by: Kerry Jones
(also exists dated 2009, see page 39)

			UNC	BU	Proof
2007	7,710,750	(38,215 proofs in sets)	£1.00	£2.00	£5.00
	46,632 of 100k	Specimen in folder		£5.00	
	10,895 of 12,500	.925 sterling silver proof			£22.00
	1,555 of 5,000	.925 sterling silver piedfort proof			£40.00
	1,250	.917 gold proof			£475.00

COMMEMORATIVE TYPE 13
1759 2009 | KEW
Chinese Pagoda
(250th Anniversary - Kew Gardens)
Design by: Christopher Le Brun

			Used	UNC/BU	Proof
2009	210,000	(34,438 proofs in sets)	£30	£40/£50	£90.00
	128,364	Specimen in folder		£80	
	7,575	.925 sterling silver proof			£150.00
	2,967	.925 sterling silver piedfort proof			£200.00
	629 of 1,000	.917 gold proof			£500.00

Prices for the Kew Gardens 50p are high due to an article in the Daily Mail online over a year ago, on the 20th February 2014 following a Royal Mint press release. Similar information was repeated by the Guardian and also featured the following day on BBC Radio 2. The article implied that they are somehow special. This caused people to pay way over the odds on eBay, which in turn meant that sellers started pricing them higher and it all got a bit out of control. The normal non proof BU coins were selling for £180 at one stage (and nearly £300 for the specimen in folder). Just a couple of days later the normal non proof coins were down to between £35 and £50. It's a repeat of the hype surrounding the dateless (2008) 20p mule error which caused that particular coin to sell for hundreds of pounds before dropping back to a more realistic £30 - £50 level (which, for most of the battered and abused coins that are sold is still too high in my opinion).

The fact that people are aware of it, will probably have a residual effect on values.

A mintage of 210,000 (it's actually 444,696 if the packaged coins and those in the BU year-sets are included) is very low compared the other Fifty-Pences that are currently in circulation, but there are plenty to go round, as there simply aren't anywhere near 444k people in the world that really want one, and one to keep, not just to turn a profit on. Wait for prices to level off before buying!

COMMEMORATIVE TYPE 14
50 PENCE
An Olympic High Jumper - Obverse dated 2009
(The young viewers of Blue Peter were invited to submit
entries for the design - This was the winner)
Design by: Florence Jackson (aged 8)
Obverse: 4

		UNC	BU
2009		£9	£18.00
	Specimen in folder		£20.00

COMMEMORATIVE TYPE 15
CELEBRATING ONE HUNDRED YEARS OF GIRLGUIDING UK | 50 | PENCE
Girl Guide emblems
(100th Anniversary - The Girl Guides)
Design by: Jonathan Evans and Donna Hainan

			UNC	BU	Proof
2010	7,410,090		FV	£1.00	
		Specimen in folder		£7.00	
	5,271	.925 sterling silver proof			£30.00
	2,879	.925 sterling silver piedfort proof			£55.00
	355	.917 gold proof			£575.00

 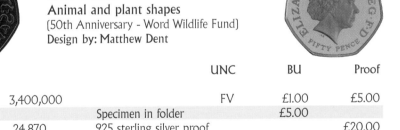

COMMEMORATIVE TYPE 16
WWF / 2011
Animal and plant shapes
(50th Anniversary - Word Wildlife Fund)
Design by: Matthew Dent

			UNC	BU	Proof
2011	3,400,000		FV	£1.00	£5.00
		Specimen in folder		£5.00	
	24,870	.925 sterling silver proof			£20.00
	2,244	.925 sterling silver piedfort proof			£40.00
	243 of 1,000	.917 gold proof			£600.00

COMMEMORATIVE TYPE 17 (Olympic 1)
50 PENCE
Swimmer
(London 2012 Olympics - Aquatics)
Design by: Jonathan Olliffe
Obverse: 4

		UNC	BU
2011	2,179,000	£1.00	£2.00
	Specimen sealed on card		£3.00

Withdrawn coin. Error - lines on face etc, right image £900.00*

* The actual error coin in the picture above was sold by Rotographic on eBay, 27th Ferbruary 2014 to the top bidder for £908.88. Not very many are known so the values are likely to vary, as and when they come up for sale. As far as I know, this is one of the highest values on record for a decimal base metal coin. Note that I've also seen a normal coin that someone had manipulated by scratching lines on the face in attempt to pass off as the withdrawn coin!

COMMEMORATIVE TYPE 18 (Olympic 2)
50 PENCE
Hand Pulling an Arrow
(London 2012 Olympics - Archery)
Design by: Piotr Powaga
Obverse: 4

		UNC	BU
2011	3,345,500	£1.00	£2.00
	Specimen sealed on card		£3.00

COMMEMORATIVE TYPE 19 (Olympic 3)
50 PENCE
An Olympic High Jumper - Obverse dated 2011
(London 2012 Olympics - Athletics, see also Commemorative type 14)
Design by: Florence Jackson (aged 8)
Obverse: 4

			UNC	BU
2011	2,224,000	Used: £2.00	£6.00	£8.00
	Specimen sealed on card			£10.00

COMMEMORATIVE TYPE 20 (Olympic 4)
50 PENCE
Shuttlecock
(London 2012 Olympics - Badminton)
Design by: Emma Kelly
Obverse: 4

		UNC	BU
2011	2,133,500	£1.00	£2.00
	Specimen sealed on card		£3.00

COMMEMORATIVE TYPE 21 (Olympic 5)
50 PENCE
Players on Ball-Textured Background
(London 2012 Olympics - Basketball)
Design by: Sarah Payne
Obverse: 4

		UNC	BU
2011	1,748,000	£1.00	£3.00
	Specimen sealed on card		£7.00
	.925 Silver Proof - See note, page 53		£20.00

COMMEMORATIVE TYPE 22 (Olympic 6)
50 PENCE
Player
(London 2012 Olympics - Boccia)
Design by: Justin Chung
Obverse: 4

		UNC	BU
2011	2,166,000	£1.00	£2.00
	Specimen sealed on card		£3.00

27.3 mm • 8.0 grammes • cupro-nickel • plain edge

COMMEMORATIVE TYPE 23 (Olympic 7)
50 PENCE
Boxing Gloves with Ring Ropes
(London 2012 Olympics - Boxing)
Design by: Shane Abery
Obverse: 4

		UNC	BU
2011	2,148,500	£1.00	£2.00
	Specimen sealed on card		£3.00

COMMEMORATIVE TYPE 24 (Olympic 8)
50 PENCE
Canoeist in Choppy Waters
(London 2012 Olympics - Canoeing)
Design by: Timothy Lees
Obverse: 4

		UNC	BU
2011	2,166,000	£1.00	£2.00
	Specimen sealed on card		£3.00

COMMEMORATIVE TYPE 25 (Olympic 9)
50 PENCE
Cyclist
(London 2012 Olympics - Cycling)
Design by: Theo Crutchley-Mack
Obverse: 4

		UNC	BU
2011	2,090,500	£1.00	£2.00
	Specimen sealed on card		£3.00
	.925 Silver Proof - See note, page 53		£20.00

COMMEMORATIVE TYPE 26 (Olympic 10)
50 PENCE
Horse, Jumping
(London 2012 Olympics - Equestrian)
Design by: Thomas Babbage
Obverse: 4

		UNC	BU
2011	2,142,500	£1.00	£2.00
	Specimen sealed on card		£3.00

COMMEMORATIVE TYPE 27 (Olympic 11)
50 PENCE
Fencing
(London 2012 Olympics - Fencing)
Design by: Ruth Summerfield
Obverse: 4

		UNC	BU
2011	2,115,500	£1.00	£2.00
	Specimen sealed on card		£3.00

COMMEMORATIVE TYPE 28 (Olympic 12)
OFFSIDE EXPLAINED / 50 PENCE
Diagram of the Offside Rule
(London 2012 Olympics - Football)
Design by: Neil Wolfson
Obverse: 4

		Used	BU
2011	1,125,500	£4.00	£8.00
	Specimen sealed on card		£10.00

COMMEMORATIVE TYPE 29 (Olympic 13)
50 PENCE
Player with Ball
(London 2012 Olympics - Goalball)
Design by: Jonathan Wren
Obverse: 4

		UNC	BU
2011	1,615,500	£1.00	£2.00
	Specimen sealed on card		£3.00

COMMEMORATIVE TYPE 30 (Olympic 14)
50 PENCE
Gymnast
(London 2012 Olympics - Gymnastics)
Design by: Jonathan Olliffe
Obverse: 4

		UNC	BU
2011	1,720,813	£1.00	£2.00
	Specimen sealed on card		£3.00

COMMEMORATIVE TYPE 31 (Olympic 15)
50 PENCE
Player with Ball
(London 2012 Olympics - Handball)
Design by: Natasha Ratcliffe
Obverse: 4

		UNC	BU
2011	1,676,500	£1.00	£2.00
	Specimen sealed on card		£3.00

COMMEMORATIVE TYPE 32 (Olympic 16)
50 PENCE
Two Hockey Players
(London 2012 Olympics - Hockey)
Design by: Robert Evans
Obverse: 4

		UNC	BU
2011	1,773,500	£1.00	£2.00
	Specimen sealed on card		£3.00

COMMEMORATIVE TYPE 33 (Olympic 17)
50 PENCE
Judo Throw
(London 2012 Olympics - Judo)
Design by: David Cornell
Obverse: 4

		Used	BU
2011	1,161,500	£4.00	£6.00
	Specimen sealed on card		£8.00

COMMEMORATIVE TYPE 34 (Olympic 18)
50 PENCE
Swimmer and four Silhouettes
(London 2012 Olympics - Modern Pentathlon)
Design by: Daniel Brittain
Obverse: 4

		UNC	BU
2011	1,689,500	£1.00	£2.00
	Specimen sealed on card		£3.00

49

27.3 mm • 8.0 grammes • cupro-nickel • plain edge

COMMEMORATIVE TYPE 35 (Olympic 19)
50 PENCE
Slogans and Two Rowers
(London 2012 Olympics - Rowing)
Design by: Davey Podmore
Obverse: 4

		UNC	BU
2011	1,717,300	£1.00	£2.00
	Specimen sealed on card		£3.00

COMMEMORATIVE TYPE 36 (Olympic 20)
50 PENCE
Sailing Boats on the Sea
(London 2012 Olympics - Sailing)
Design by: Bruce Rushin
Obverse: 4

		UNC	BU
2011	1,749,500	£1.00	£2.00
	Specimen sealed on card		£3.00

COMMEMORATIVE TYPE 37 (Olympic 21)
50 PENCE
Figure, Shooting
(London 2012 Olympics - Shooting)
Design by: Pravin Dewdhory
Obverse: 4

		UNC	BU
2011	1,656,500	£1.00	£2.00
	Specimen sealed on card		£3.00

COMMEMORATIVE TYPE 38 (Olympic 22)
50 PENCE
Table Tennis Bats, Ball etc
(London 2012 Olympics - Table Tennis)
Design by: Alan Linsdell
Obverse: 4

		UNC	BU
2011	1,737,500	£1.00	£2.00
	Specimen sealed on card		£3.00

COMMEMORATIVE TYPE 39 (Olympic 23)
50 PENCE
Two Figures Participating in Taekwando
(London 2012 Olympics - Taekwando)
Design by: David Gibbons
Obverse: 4

		UNC	BU
2011	1,664,000	£1.00	£2.00
	Specimen sealed on card		£3.00

COMMEMORATIVE TYPE 40 (Olympic 24)
50 PENCE
Tennis Ball and Net
(London 2012 Olympics - Tennis)
Design by: Tracy Baines
Obverse: 4

		UNC	BU
2011	1,454,000	£1.00	£2.00
	Specimen sealed on card		£3.00

COMMEMORATIVE TYPE 41 (Olympic 25)
50 PENCE
Silhouettes of Runner, Cyclist and Swimmer
(London 2012 Olympics - Triathlon)
Design by: Sarah Harvey
Obverse: 4

		Used	BU
2011	1,163,500	£5.50	£7.00
	Specimen sealed on card		£10.00

COMMEMORATIVE TYPE 42 (Olympic 26)
50 PENCE
Three Players and Central Net
(London 2012 Olympics - Volleyball)
Design by: Daniela Boothman
Obverse: 4

		UNC	BU
2011	2,133,500	£1.00	£2.00
	Specimen sealed on card		£3.00

COMMEMORATIVE TYPE 43 (Olympic 27)
50 PENCE
Basic Outline of a Weightlifter
(London 2012 Olympics - Weightlifting)
Design by: Rob Shakespeare
Obverse: 4

		UNC	BU
2011	1,879,000	£1.00	£2.00
	Specimen sealed on card		£3.00

COMMEMORATIVE TYPE 44 (Olympic 28)
50 PENCE
Man Playing, Ball in Lap
(London 2012 Olympics - Wheelchair Rugby)
Design by: Natasha Ratcliffe
Obverse: 4

		UNC	BU
2011	1,765,500	£1.00	£2.00
	Specimen sealed on card		£3.00
	.925 Silver Proof - See note, page 53		£20.00

COMMEMORATIVE TYPE 45 (Olympic 29)
50 PENCE
Wrestlers
(London 2012 Olympics - Wrestling)
Design by: Roderick Enriquez
Obverse: 4

		Used	BU
2011	1,129,500	£3.00	£6.00
	Specimen sealed on card		£8.00

Olympic 30
Medallion Only
The Royal Mint issued a medallion with the 29x 50p coins. It's not a coin, but is mentioned here for completeness. Values are around £20.

The 50p Olympic Coins - Silver Proofs?

Noted so far in silver proof form are: Basketball, Cycling and Wheelchair Rugby. The Royal Mint apparently also made three 'sets' of six silver proof coins which included the Fencing, Badminton, Basketball, Hockey, Tennis and the, I quote, 'wildly popular' football coin!

Gold Versions: Gold proofs were struck by the Royal Mint and just given to the designers of the coins. They are therefore extremely rare!

27.3 mm • 8.0 grammes • cupro-nickel • plain edge

FIFTY PENCE / 50
Ironside's rejected design for the original 50p
(This is what the original 50p could have looked like)
Design by: Christopher Ironside
Obverse: 4

		UNC	BU	Proof
2013	7,000,000	£1.00	£3.00	£10.00
	Specimen in folder, price new		£8.00	
4,500 max	.925 sterling silver proof, price new			£45.00
1,500 max	.925 sterling silver piedfort proof, price new			£90.00
340 max	.917 gold proof, price new			£700.00

BENJAMIN / COMPOSER BORN 1913 / BRITTEN
His name in a double stave,
'Blow Bugle blow' and 'Set the
wild echoes flying'.
(To mark the centenary of the birth
of Benjamin Britten)
Design by: Tom Phillips

		UNC	BU	Proof
2013	5,300,000	£1.00	£3.00	£10.00
	Specimen in folder		£9.00	
2000 max	.925 sterling silver proof, price new			£45.00
1000 max	.925 sterling silver piedfort proof, price new			£90.00
150 max	.917 gold proof, price new			£700.00

XX / COMMONWEALTH GAMES GLASGOW / 2014
Male cyclist and female runner
(To commemorate the 20th Commonwealth
Games)
Design by: Alex Loudon and Dan Flashman

		UNC	BU	Proof
2014		£1.00	£4.00	£15.00
	Specimen in folder, price new		£10.00	
2500 max	.925 sterling silver proof, price new			£50.00
1000 max	.925 sterling silver piedfort proof, price new			£100.00
260 max	.917 gold proof, price new			£725.00

THE BATTLE OF BRITAIN 1940
(Pilots scrambling, planes in flight above)
Design by: Gary Breeze
Obverse: 4

Note that the denomination is omited on the coin from the 2015 year set, shown here. The Royal Mint state that the coins made for circulation will show the denomination. And probably also bear the new portrait of the Queen?

	UNC	BU	Proof
2015 (only in BU sets so far)			£15.00
Specimen in folder, price new		£10.00	

Silver and gold proof versions don't seem to be available at time of writing.

What's currently legal tender?

All £1 coins are legal tender. The £1 coin is the most commonly forged coin, with estimates o
between 2-3% of the total £1 coins in circulation being forgeries. Look out for poor definition an
mis-matching edges or reverses (i.e a Welsh reverse with a date that should have an English obverse
and/or a coin with edge lettering that doesn't match the country represented on its reverse). I
someone gives you a fake £1 coin, you are not legally obliged to accept it.

Which are hard to find?

The hardest £1 coin to be found in circulation are the 1998 and 1999 as they were only made fo
year sets. The 1988 has a relatively low mintage of just over seven million which doesn't make it rar
but it's certainly the scarcest in comparison to the others. The 2011 Edinburgh coin has a mintag
of under one million and often sells for more than face value, even in used condition.

OBVERSE

OBVERSE 1
(used 1983 - 1984)
D•G•REG•F•D•(date) || ELIZABETH II
Elizabeth II, Dei Gratia Regina, Fidei Defensor
(Elizabeth II, By the Grace of God Queen and Defender of the Faith)
Portrait by: Arnold Machin

OBVERSE 2
(used 1985 - 1997)
ELIZABETH II || D•G•REG•F•D•(date)
Elizabeth II, Dei Gratia Regina, Fidei Defensor
(Elizabeth II, By the Grace of God Queen and Defender of the Faith)
Portrait by: Raphael Maklouf

OBVERSE 3
(used 1998 - 2008)
ELIZABETH II•D•G || REG•F•D•(date)
Elizabeth II, Dei Gratia Regina, Fidei Defensor
(Elizabeth II, By the Grace of God Queen and Defender of the Faith)
Portrait by: Ian Rank-Broadley

OBVERSE 4 (similar to last, with no rim beading)
(used 2008 to date)
ELIZABETH II•D•G || REG•F•D•(date)
Elizabeth II, Dei Gratia Regina, Fidei Defensor
(Elizabeth II, By the Grace of God Queen and Defender of the Faith)
Portrait by: Ian Rank-Broadley

1983 UK Royal Arms design by Eric Sewell

	UNC	BU	Proof
443,053,510	£1.50	£2.00	£5.00
484,900 Specimen in folder		£2.50	
50,000 .925 sterling silver proof			£25.00
10,000 .925 sterling silver piedfort proof			£115.00

The following 4 coins ("Coronet" series) were designed by Leslie Durbin.

1984 Scottish Thistle in Coronet

	UNC	BU	Proof
146,256,501	£1.50	£2.00	£5.00
27,960 Specimen in folder		£2.50	
44,855 .925 sterling silver proof			£20.00
15,000 .925 sterling silver piedfort proof			£30.00

1985 Welsh Leek in Coronet

	UNC	BU	Proof
228,430,749	£1.50	£2.00	£5.00
24,850 Specimen in folder		£2.50	
50,000 .925 sterling silver proof			£20.00
15,000 .925 sterling silver piedfort proof			£30.00

1986 N.I. Flax in Coronet

	UNC	BU	Proof
10,409,501	£1.50	£2.00	£5.00
19,908 Specimen in folder		£2.50	
37,958 .925 sterling silver proof			£20.00
15,000 .925 sterling silver piedfort proof			£30.00

1987 English Oak in Coronet

	UNC	BU	Proof
39,298,502	£1.50	£2.00	£5.00
72,607 Specimen in folder		£2.50	
50,500 .925 sterling silver proof			£20.00
15,000 .925 sterling silver piedfort proof			£30.00

|

1988 Royal Shield design (UK) by Derek Gorringe

		UNC	BU	Proof
7,118,825	Used: £1.50	£3.00	£4.00	£5.00
29,550	Specimen in folder		£5.00	
50,000	.925 sterling silver proof			£25.00
10,000	.925 sterling silver piedfort proof			£30.00

The following 4 coins ("Coronet" series) were designed by Leslie Durbin.

1989 Scottish Thistle in Coronet

70,580,501		£1.50	£2.00	£5.00
25,000	.925 sterling silver proof			£20.00
10,000	.925 sterling silver piedfort proof			£30.00

1990 Welsh Leek in Coronet

97,269,302		£1.50	£2.00	£5.00
25,000	.925 sterling silver proof			£20.00
10,000	.925 sterling silver piedfort proof			£30.00

1991 N.I. Flax in Coronet

38,443,575		£1.50	£2.00	£5.00
25,000	.925 sterling silver proof			£20.00
10,000	.925 sterling silver piedfort proof			£30.00

1992 English Oak in Coronet

36,320,487		£1.50	£2.00	£5.00
25,000	.925 sterling silver proof			£20.00
10,000	.925 sterling silver piedfort proof			£30.00

1993	UK Royal Arms design by Eric Sewell	UNC	BU	Proof
114,744,500		£1.50	£2.00	£5.00
484,900	Specimen in folder		£2.510	
50,000	.925 sterling silver proof			£20.00
10,000	.925 sterling silver piedfort proof			£30.00

The following 4 coins ("Heraldic" series) were designed by Norman Sillman.

1994	Scottish Lion Rampant	UNC	BU	Proof
29,752,525		£1.50	£2.00	£5.00
	Specimen in folder		£2.50	
25,000	.925 sterling silver proof			£20.00
11,722	.925 sterling silver piedfort proof			£30.00

1995	Welsh Dragon	UNC	BU	Proof
34,503,501		£1.50	£2.00	£5.00
	Specimen in folder		£2.50	
	Specimen in folder (Welsh text)		£8.00	
27,445	.925 sterling silver proof			£20.00
8,458	.925 sterling silver piedfort proof			£30.00

1996	N.I. Celtic Cross	UNC	BU	Proof
89,886,000		£1.50	£2.00	£5.00
	Specimen in folder		£2.50	
25,000	.925 sterling silver cased proof			£20.00
10,000	.925 sterling silver piedfort cased proof			£30.00

1997	English Three Lions	UNC	BU	Proof
57,117,450		£1.50	£2.00	£5.00
	Specimen in folder		£2.50	
20,137	.925 sterling silver proof			£20.00
10,000	.925 sterling silver piedfort proof			£30.00

		UNC	BU	Proof
1998	UK Royal Arms design by Eric Sewell			
(BU packs only)			£10.00	£10.00
13,843	.925 sterling silver proof			£25.00
10,000	.925 sterling silver piedfort proof			£35.00
1999	Scottish Lion Rampant			
(BU packs only)			£10.00	£10.00
25,000	.925 sterling silver proof			£25.00
2,000	.925 sterling "Special Frosted Finish" proof			£35.00
10,000	.925 sterling silver piedfort proof			£35.00
2000	Welsh Dragon			
109,496,500		£1.50	£2.50	£5.00
40,000	.925 sterling silver proof			£25.00
2,000	.925 sterling "Special Frosted Finish" proof			£35.00
10,000	.925 sterling silver piedfort proof			£35.00
2001	N.I. Celtic Cross			
58,093,731		£1.50	£2.50	£5.00
13,237	.925 sterling silver proof			£25.00
2,000	.925 sterling "Special Frosted Finish" proof			£35.00
8,464	.925 sterling silver piedfort proof			£35.00
2002	English Three Lions			
77,818,000		£1.50	£2.50	£5.00
17,693	.925 sterling silver proof			£25.00
2,000	.925 sterling "Special Frosted Finish" proof			£35.00
6,599	.925 sterling silver piedfort proof			£35.00
2003	UK Royal Arms design by Eric Sewell			
61,596,500		£1.50	£2.50	£5.00
15,830	.925 sterling silver proof			£25.00
9,871	.925 sterling silver piedfort proof			£35.00

The following 4 coins ("Bridge" series) were designed by Edwina Ellis. The edges all feature a decorative pattern.

2004   Scotland - Forth Bridge

		UNC	BU	Proof
39,162,000		£1.50	£2.00	£5.00
24,014	Specimen in folder		£3.00	
11,470	.925 sterling silver proof			£25.00
7,013	.925 sterling silver piedfort cased proof			£35.00
2,618	.917 gold proof			£500.00

2005   Wales - Menai Bridge

99,429,500		£1.50	£2.00	£5.00
24,802	Specimen in folder		£3.00	
8,371	.925 sterling silver proof			£25.00
6,007	.925 sterling silver piedfort cased proof			£40.00
1,195	.917 gold proof			£500.00

2006   Northern Ireland - Egyptian Arch

38,938,000		£1.50	£2.00	£5.00
23,856	Specimen in folder		£3.00	
14,765	.925 sterling silver proof			£28.00
5,129	.925 sterling silver piedfort cased proof			£40.00
728	.917 gold proof			£550.00

2007   England - Millenium Bridge

26,180,160		£1.50	£2.00	£5.00
5,326	Specimen in folder		£5.00	
10,110	.925 sterling silver proof			£28.00
5,739	.925 sterling silver piedfort cased proof			£40.00
1,122	.917 gold proof			£550.00

1983 to 2008 UK, English and NI reverse designs and also the 2008 onwards shield reverse type carry the edge inscription:
DECUS ET TUTAMEN (An ornament and a safeguard)

1984 to 1999 Scottish reverse designs carry the edge inscription:
NEMO ME IMPUNE LACESSIT (No-one provokes me with impunity)

1985 to 2000 Welsh reverse designs carry the edge inscription:
PLEIDIOL WYF I'M GWLAD (True am I to my country)

61

2008   UK Royal Arms design by: Eric Sewell. With Obverse 3.

		UNC	BU	Proof
3,910,000		£1.50	£2.00	£6.00
9,134	.925 sterling silver proof			£30.00
7,894	.925 sterling silver piedfort cased proof			£45.00
2,005	Set of 14 £1 coins, all designs 1983 - 2008. Silver with gold coloured 'silhouette' details. All dated 2008			£450.00
	As above, as gold proof set			-

Large shield part of the UK Royal coat of Arms by: Matthew Dent. With Obverse 4. Struck annually.

2008	43,827,300	£1.50	£2.00	£8.00
5,000	.925 sterling silver proof			£30.00
2,456	.925 sterling piedfort proof			£50.00
860	.917 gold proof			£600.00

2009				
	27,625,600	£1.50	£2.00	£8.00
	.925 sterling silver proof from set			£30.00
	.917 gold proof			£600.00
2010	57,120,000	£1.50	£2.00	£8.00
2011	25,415,000	£1.50	£2.00	£8.00
2012	35,700,030	£1.50	£2.00	£8.00
2013	13,090,500	£1.50	£2.00	£8.00
	.925 sterling silver proof			£40.00
2014		£1.50	£2.00	£8.00
2015		£1.50	£2.00	£8.00

The following 4 coins ("Capital Cities" series) were designed by Stuart Devlin and all use Obverse 4.

2010

Edge: PRO TANTO QUID RETRIBUAMUS

	UNC	BU	Proof
6,205,000	£1.50	£2.00	£7.00
.925 sterling silver proof			£40.00
.925 sterling silver piedfort proof			£80.00

2010

Edge: DOMINE DIRIGE NOS

	UNC	BU	Proof
2,635,000	£1.50	£2.00	£7.00
.925 sterling silver proof			£40.00
.925 sterling silver piedfort proof			£80.00

2011

Edge: Y DDRAIS GOCH DDYRY CYCHWYN

	UNC	BU	Proof
1,615,000	£2.00	£3.00	£7.00
.925 sterling silver proof			£40.00
.925 sterling silver piedfort proof			£80.00

2011

Edge: NISI DOMINUS FRUSTRA

		UNC	BU	Proof
935,000	Used: £3.00	£5.00	£7.00	£12.00
.925 sterling silver proof				£40.00
.925 sterling silver piedfort proof				£80.00

2013 National Floral Symbols series - England, by Timothy Noad
Edge: DECUS ET TUTAMEN

	UNC	BU	Proof
5,270,000	£2.00	£5.00	£10.00
.925 sterling silver proof			£50.00
.925 sterling silver piedfort proof			£100.00

2013 National Floral Symbols series - Wales by Timothy Noad
Edge: PLEIDIOL WYF I'M GWLAD

	UNC	BU	Proof
5,270,000	£2.00	£5.00	£10.00
.925 sterling silver proof			
.925 sterling silver piedfort proof			£50.00

? 2013 Silver proof version of the 1988 design			£100.00
? 2013 Silver proof version of the 1983 design			£100.00

2014 National Floral Symbols series - Scotland, by Timothy Noad
Edge: NEMO ME IMPUNE LACESSIT

	£2.00	£3.00	£10.00
.925 sterling silver proof			
.925 sterling silver piedfort proof			£100.00

2014 National Floral Symbols series - N. Ireland, by Timothy Noad
Edge: DECUS ET TUTAMEN

	£2.00	£3.00	£5.00
.925 sterling silver proof			
.925 sterling silver piedfort proof			£100.00

2015: No commemorative £1 coin has been struck for 2015 (at time
of going to press).

What's currently legal tender?

All £2 coins dated from 1986 to date are legal tender. The earlier single metal type coins dated 1986 to 1996 are not often seen in circulation and therefore may not be accepted by some merchants who are unfamiliar with them.

Which are hard to find?

All of the 1986 to 1996 (single alloy) £2 coins are now hard to find in circulation. The scarcest £2 coin is probably COMMEMORATIVE TYPE 3, the 'Claim of Right' coin, as this was minted in much smaller quantities than the other 1989 £2 coin, and was only issued in Scotland. The bi-metallic coin with the 'Queen wearing a necklace' was never rare. Some of the more recent £2 coins do sell for more than face value, even in used condition! See listings.

COMMEMORATIVE TYPE 1

A thistle encircled by a laurel wreath, superimposed on St. Andrew's Cross
(1986 Commonwealth Games, Edinburgh)
Reverse design by: Norman Sillman
Edge: XIII COMMONWEALTH
GAMES SCOTLAND 1986

			UNC	BU	Proof
1986	8,212,184	104,591 Proofs	£3.00	£7.50	£10.00
		Specimen in folder		£8.00	
	58,881	.500 silver UNC	£15.00		
	59,779	.925 sterling silver proof			£22.00
		.917 gold proof			£450.00

COMMEMORATIVE TYPE 2

Intertwined W & M (monogrammes of William & Mary)
House of Commons Mace, English Crown
TERCENTENARY of the BILL of RIGHTS
1689-1989
Design by: John Lobban
Edge: MILLED

			UNC	BU	Proof
1989	4,777,891 Inc T3	84,704 Proofs	£3.00	£10.00	£15.00
		Partially non frosted proof*			£18.00
		Specimen in folder		£11.00	
	25,000	.925 sterling silver proof			£22.00
	10,000	.925 sterling silver, piedfort proof			£30.00

*Proofs that were part of a Bass Charington promotion appear to have a non frosted bust of the Queen. More comparison is needed at this stage.

COMMEMORATIVE TYPE 3
Intertwined W & M
(monogram of William & Mary)
House of Commons Mace, Scottish Crown
TERCENTENARY of the CLAIM of RIGHT
1689-1989
Design by: John Lobban
Edge: MILLED

			Used	UNC	Proof
1989	Inc. with T2	84,704 Proofs	£16.00	£20.00	£25.00
		Specimen in folder		£20.00	
	Specimen folder, including both versions ('Bill' & 'Claim')		£30.00		
	24,852	.925 sterling silver proof			£40.00
	10,000	.925 sterling silver, Piedfort proof			£40.00

COMMEMORATIVE TYPE 4
Intertwined W & M
(monogram of William & Mary)
Britannia Seated
BANK of ENGLAND 1694-1994
Design by: Leslie Durbin
Edge: SIC VOS NON VOBIS

			UNC	BU	Proof
1994	1,443,116	67,721 Proofs	£3.00	£7.50	£10.00
		Specimen in folder		£9.00	
	27,957	.925 sterling silver proof			£22.00
	9,569	.925 sterling silver, Piedfort proof			£30.00
	1,000	.917 gold proof			£500.00
	Not known	Gold proof mule with wrong obverse*			£1700.00

*The obverse of the double sovereign type £2 coin was used in error. The Queen's head is larger, it breaks the more abbreviated legend at the top and the words 'TWO POUNDS' are not present.

COMMEMORATIVE TYPE 5
Dove of Peace
(Commemorating 50 years' peace,
since the end of World War II)
Reverse design by: John Mills
Edge: 1945 IN PEACE GOODWILL 1995

			UNC	BU	Proof
1995	4,388,006	60,639 Proofs	£3.00	£7.50	£10.00
		Specimen in folder		£9.00	
	50,000	.925 sterling silver proof			£22.00
	10,000	.925 sterling silver, Piedfort proof			£30.00
	2,500	.917 gold proof			£500.00

COMMEMORATIVE TYPE 6
UN logo, array of flags
NATIONS UNITED FOR PEACE 1945 - 1995
(50th Anniversary - United Nations)
Design by: Michael Rizzello
Edge: MILLED

			UNC	BU	Proof
1995	Inc. with T5		£3.00	£7.50	£10.00
		Specimen in folder		£9.00	
	175,000	.925 sterling silver proof			£25.00
	10,000	.925 sterling silver Piedfort proof			£30.00
	2,098	.917 gold proof			£500.00

COMMEMORATIVE TYPE 7
Football design, with date, 1996, in centre
(10th European Championship)
Design by: John Mills
Edge: TENTH EUROPEAN CHAMPIONSHIP

			UNC	BU	Proof
1996	5,141,350		£3.00	£7.50	£10.00
	84,704	Specimen in folder		£9.00	
	50,000	.925 sterling silver proof			£20.00
	10,000	.925 sterling silver, Piedfort proof			£30.00
	2,098	.917 gold proof			£500.00

OBVERSE

OBVERSE 1
(used 1997 only)
ELIZABETH II DEI GRA REGINA F D
Elizabeth II, Dei Gratia Regina, Fidei Defensor
(Elizabeth II, By the Grace of God Queen and Defender of the Faith)
Portrait by: Raphael Maklouf

OBVERSE 2
(used 1998 to date)
Also used on commemoratives 8 to 17, 19 and 32)
ELIZABETH II DEI GRATIA REGINA FID DEF
Elizabeth II, Dei Gratia Regina, Fidei Defensor
(Elizabeth II, By the Grace of God Queen and Defender of the Faith)
Portrait by: Ian Rank-Broadley

OBVERSE 2b   **OBVERSE 2c**   **OBVERSE 2d**

Variations of obverse 2 - Some of the later reverse designs don't include a date, the face value or both, so these have been incorporated into the obverse legend.

2b 'TWO POUNDS' at bottom - was used for Commemorative Types
18, 20, 24, 28, 29, 30, 31 & 33
2c DATE at bottom - was used for Commemorative Types 21, 22, 23 and 25
2d 'TWO POUNDS' and DATE at bottom - was used for Commemorative Types 26, 27 & 34

REVERSE

REVERSE 1 (the standard non-commemorative reverse)
(used 1997 to date)
Rings, representing stages of development:
from centre, outward: IRON AGE, INDUSTRIAL REVOLUTION
(cogs), ELECTRONIC AGE (silicon chips), INTERNET AGE
Edge: STANDING ON THE SHOULDERS OF GIANTS
Design by: Bruce Rushin

TRIAL TYPES
Sailing ship, probably representing the Golden Hind
A first Bi-metallic coin trial. Coins are dated 1994 but were actually released in 1998. The coins were all issued in packs which also contain examples of the outer and inner blanks and a nickel-brass ring. The obverse used is a modified OBVERSE 1 - very similar, but the trial obverse actually has a dot instead of a small cross between the 'D' and 'ELIZABETH'. The obverse lettering also appears weaker and slightly thinner than usual.
Edge: DECUS ET TUTAMEN ANNO REGNI XLVI
Value: The bi-metallic pack tends to sell for between £60 and £80.

Single metal £2 trial, dated 1994 and marked 'ROYAL MINT TRIAL' on both sides, also featuring the ship design.
These are very rare. Value £500.00 - £2000.00

TYPE 1 (obverse 1, reverse 1)

			UNC	BU	Proof
1997	13,734,625		£3.00	£4.00	£7.50
		Specimen in folder		£9.00	
	29,910	.925 silver proof			£20.00
	10,000	.925 silver piedfort proof			£40.00
	2,482	.917 gold proof			£450.00

TYPE 2 (obverse 2, reverse 1)

			UNC	BU	Proof
1998	91,110,375	100,000	FV	£4.00	£7.50
1999*	38,652,000		£40.00	?£100.00?	
2000	25,770,000		FV	£4.00	£7.50
2001	34,984,750		FV	£4.00	£7.50
2002	13,024,750		FV	£4.00	£7.50
2003	17,531,250		FV	£4.00	£7.50
2004	11,981,500		FV	£4.00	£7.50
2005	3,837,250		FV	£4.00	£7.50
2006	16,715,000		FV	£4.00	£7.50
2007	10,270,000		FV	£4.00	£7.50
2008	30,107,000		FV	£4.00	£7.50
2009	8,775,000		FV	£4.00	£7.50
2010	6,890,000		FV	£4.00	£7.50
2011	24,375,030		FV	£4.00	£7.50
2012	3,900,000		FV	£4.00	£7.50
2013	15,860,250		FV	£4.00	£7.50
2014			FV	£10.00	£10.00
2015			FV	£10.00	£10.00

* 1999 was not issued as a proof or in BU sets and is therefore scarce to almost unheard of in top condition, despite the high mintage.

28.40 mm • 12.0 grammes • bi-metal • various edge

COMMEMORATIVE TYPE 8
Symbolic representation of a stadium with rugby
ball and goalposts. '1999' above, 'TWO POUNDS' below
(1999 Rugby World Cup)
Design by: Ron Dutton
Edge: RUGBY WORLD CUP 1999

			UNC	BU	Proof
1999	4,933,000		£3.00	£7.50	£10.00
		Specimen in folder		£9.00	
	9,665	.925 sterling silver proof			£22.00
	10,000	.925 sterling silver hologram Piedfort proof			£75.00
	311	.917 gold proof			£450.00

COMMEMORATIVE TYPE 9
Symbolic representation of Marconi's successful
transatlantic wireless transmission of 1901,
'TWO POUNDS' below
Design by: Robert Evans
Edge: WIRELESS BRIDGES THE ATLANTIC...MARCONI 1901...

			UNC	BU	Proof
2001	4,558,000		£3.00	£7.50	£10.00
		Specimen in folder		£9.00	
	11,488	.925 sterling silver proof			£22.00
	6,759	.925 sterling silver Piedfort proof			£40.00
	1,658	.917 gold proof			£450.00

a   b   c   d

COMMEMORATIVE TYPE 10
XVII COMMONWEALTH GAMES 2002
around athlete holding banner, (1 of 4) national flags
(27th Commonwealth Games, Manchester)
Design by: Matthew Bonaccorsi
Edge: SPIRIT OF FRIENDSHIP MANCHESTER 2002

			Used	UNC/BU	Proof
2002	650,500	10-a English flag	£6.00	£20/£30	£35.00
	485,500	10-b N. Ireland flag	£20.00	£30/£40	£45.00
	771,750	10-c Scottish flag	£5.00	£10/£20	£25.00
	588,500	10-d Welsh flag	£8.00	£20/£30	£35.00

These coins, being newly 'discovered' as those with the lowest mintages of all the circulating £2 coins tend to sell for more than face value, even in used condition! Certainly worth looking out for in your change, especially the NI coin which looks very similar to the England coin but has a crowned hand in the centre.

Sets of the 4 Type 10 coins:	Specimens in folder	£90.00
47,895	base metal proof set	£100.00
2,553	.925 sterling silver proof set	£170.00
3,497	.925 sterling silver Piedfort set (coloured flags)	£250.00
315	.917 gold proof set	£1,800.00

COMMEMORATIVE TYPE 11
DNA Double Helix pattern, DNA DOUBLE HELIX,
1953 TWO POUNDS 2003
(50th Anniversary - Discovery of DNA)
Design by: John Mills
Edge: DEOXYRIBONUCLEIC ACID

			UNC	BU	Proof
2003	4,299,000		£3.00	£7.50	£10.00
	41,568	Specimen in folder		£9.00	
	11,204	.925 sterling silver proof			£30.00
	8,728	.925 sterling silver Piedfort proof			£50.00
	1,500	.917 gold proof			£500.00

COMMEMORATIVE TYPE 12
Steam locomotive TWO POUNDS R.TREVITHICK
1804 INVENTION INDUSTRY PROGRESS 2004
(200th anniversary - Steam Locomotive)
Design by: Robert Lowe
Edge: pattern of arcs & curves, representing viaducts

			UNC	BU	Proof
2004	5,004,500		£3.00	£7.50	£10.00
	56,871	Specimen in folder		£9.00	
	10,233 of 25k	.925 sterling silver proof			£22.00
	5,303 of 10k	.925 sterling silver Piedfort cased proof			£40.00
	1,500	.917 gold proof			£500.00

COMMEMORATIVE TYPE 13
Swords, Maces, Croziers in a starbust pattern,
1605-2005, TWO POUNDS
(400th anniversary - Gunpowder Plot)
Design by: Peter Forster
Edge: REMEMBER REMEMBER THE FIFTH OF NOVEMBER*

			UNC	BU	Proof
2005	5,140,500		£3.00	£7.50	£10.00
	47,895	Specimen in folder		£9.00	
	4,394	.925 sterling silver proof			£22.00
	4,584	.925 sterling silver Piedfort proof			£50.00
	914	.917 gold proof			£550.00

* These very often end up having missing tails on the 'R's of the edge lettering, so that they can in extreme cases read PEMEMBEP PEMEMBEP THE FIFTH OF NOVEMBEP. This problem with certain edge letters has also been noted on some other £2 and £1 coins. It makes them a little more interesting, but it is my opinion that such errors should have no real affect on the value, especially at such a young stage in a coins' life! I say should have no real influence on the value, but it seems it does have an affect on value, at least on eBay, where PEMEMBER coins in normal used condition seem to be exchanging hands for £10 and examples in UNC or near to UNC condition have been sold for £20 - £30. Judging by the number of them that is constantly available, I can't really see the value of this this minor error increasing much in the future - assuming of course that the media don't stir up a frenzy akin to the dateless 20p, the Kew Gardens 50p and most recently the Royal Navy £2!

COMMEMORATIVE TYPE 14
St. Paul's Cathedral, floodlit with spotlights.
1945-2005, TWO POUNDS
(60th anniversary - End of World War II)
Design by: Robert Elderton
Edge: IN VICTORY: MAGNANIMITY, IN PEACE: GOODWILL

			UNC	BU	Proof
2005	10,191,000		£3.00	£10.00	
	53,686	Specimen in folder		£12.00	
	Specimen folder (including special edition medallion)			£20.00	
	21,734	.925 sterling silver proof			£25.00
	Not Known	*Error edge: REMEMBER REMEMBER THE FIFTH OF NOVEMBER .925 silver proof, as above			£400.00?
	4,798	.925 sterling silver Piedfort proof			£40.00
	2,924	.917 gold proof			£500.00

* The error edge 60th Anniversary of the End of WWII £2 coin has obviously ended up with the edge inscription of the other themed £2 coin struck that year to commemorate the gunpowder plot! The author has only been informed about one such coin and was lucky enough to have been given the opportunity to purchase it. There may be others, (see also Type 18) and the fact that the mint made this error with a proof coin may also indicate that normal 'business' struck coins might suffer from the same error. And what about the piedfort and/or gold proof versions? This is one of those discoveries that can make new coins interesting! I'd be interested to hear if any other readers come across another example of the error edge inscription coins. Update 2015: no others have been reported in over 5 years.

COMMEMORATIVE TYPE 15
Portrait of Isambard Kingdom Brunel in front of machinery
TWO POUNDS | 2006
(200th anniversary - Birth of Isambard Kingdom Brunel)
Design by: Rod Kelly
Edge: 1806-59 . ISAMBARD KINGDOM BRUNEL . ENGINEER

			UNC	BU	Proof
2006	7,928,250		£3.00	£7.50	£10.00
	54,564	Specimen in folder		£9.00	
	7,251 of 20k	.925 sterling silver proof			£25.00
	3,199 of 5k	.925 sterling silver Piedfort proof			£35.00
	1,071 of 1,500	.917 gold proof			£550.00

28.40 mm • 12.0 grammes • bi-metal • various edge

COMMEMORATIVE TYPE 16
Representation of the engineering achievements of I.K.Brunel,
2006 | BRUNEL | TWO POUNDS
(200th anniversary - Birth of Isambard Kingdom Brunel)
Design by: Robert Evans
Edge: SO MANY IRONS IN THE FIRE

			UNC	BU	Proof
2006	7,452,250		£3.00	£7.50	£10.00
	12,694	Specimen in folder		£9.00	
	5,375 of 20k	.925 sterling silver proof			£25.00
	Not Known	.925 sterling silver proof with no edge lettering			£300.00?
	3,018 of 5k	.925 sterling silver Piedfort proof			£35.00
	746 of 1,500	.917 gold proof			£500.00

COMMEMORATIVE TYPE 17
Jigsaw pieces of the English rose and Scotish thistle,
TWO | 2007 | POUNDS | 1707
(300th anniversary - Act of Union between England and Scotland)
Design by: Yvonne Holton
Edge: UNITED INTO ONE KINGDOM

			UNC	BU	Proof
2007	7,545,000		£3.00	£7.50	£10.00
	8,863	Specimen in folder		£9.00	
	8,310	.925 sterling silver proof			£25.00
	4,000	.925 sterling silver Piedfort proof			£40.00
	750	.917 gold proof			£500.00

COMMEMORATIVE TYPE 18
Five link chain with broken link as the nought in 1807,
AN ACT FOR THE ABOLITION OF THE SLAVE TRADE | 2007
(200th anniversary - Abolition of the British slave trade)
Design by: David Gentleman
Edge: AM I NOT A MAN AND A BROTHER
Obverse: 2b

			UNC	BU	Proof
2007	8,445,000	(no 'DG' initials)	£3.00	£7.50	£10.00*
	8,688	Specimen in folder ('DG' to right of chain)	£14.00		
	7,095	.925 sterling silver proof ('DG' to right of chain)			£25.00
	3,990	.925 sterling silver Piedfort proof			£40.00
	1000 max	.917 gold proof			£500.00

* A proof version of this coin is known to exist with the 'THE 4TH OLYMPIAD LONDON
edge legend, obviously meant for Type 19. See also the note under Type 14.

COMMEMORATIVE TYPE 19
Running Track
LONDON OLYMPIC CENTENARY | 1908 | TWO POUNDS | 2008
(Centenary - 1908 London Olympics)
Design by: Thomas T Docherty
Edge: THE 4TH OLYMPIAD LONDON
Obverse: 2

			Used	BU	Proof
2008	910,000		£4.00	£12.00	£15.00
	29,594 of 100k	Specimen in folder		£20.00	
	6,841 of 20k	.925 sterling silver proof			£30.00
	1,619 of 2,000	.925 sterling silver Piedfort proof			£45.00
	1,908	.917 gold proof			£500.00

COMMEMORATIVE TYPE 20
Olympic flag and two hands
BEIJING 2008 | LONDON 2012
(Olympic handover ceremony)
Design by: Royal Mint in House
Edge: I CALL UPON THE YOUTH OF THE WORLD
Obverse: 2b

			Used	BU	Proof
2008	918,000		£4.00	£15.00	
	47,765 of 250k	Specimen in folder		£20.00	
	30,000	.925 sterling silver proof			£40.00
	3,000	.925 sterling silver Piedfort proof			£50.00
	3,250	.917 gold proof			£500.00

COMMEMORATIVE TYPE 21
Darwin facing ape
1809 DARWIN 2009 | TWO POUNDS
(200th anniversay - birth of Charles Darwin)
Design by: Suzie Zamit
Edge: ON THE ORIGIN OF SPECIES 1859
Obverse: 2c

			UNC	BU	Proof
2009	3,903,000		£3.00	£7.50	£10.00
	25,000 max	Specimen in folder		£9.00	
	9,357	.925 sterling silver proof			£30.00
	3,282	.925 sterling silver Piedfort proof			£75.00
	1000	.917 gold proof			£550.00

COMMEMORATIVE TYPE 22
Burns quote
1759 ROBERT BURNS 1796 | TWO POUNDS
(250 years anniversay - birth of Robert Burns)
Design by: Royal Mint in House
Edge: SHOULD AULD ACQUAINTANCE BE FORGOT
Obverse: 2c

			Used	BU	Proof
2009	3,253,000		£3.50	£8.00	£15.00
		Specimen in folder		£12.00	
	9,188	.925 sterling silver proof			£30.00
	3,500	.925 sterling silver Piedfort proof			£45.00
	1000	.917 gold proof			£600.00

COMMEMORATIVE TYPE 23
Nurses hands feeling for a pulse
1820 - FLORENCE NIGHTINGALE - 1910 | TWO POUNDS
(150 years of modern nursing and to the centenary of the
death of Florence Nightingale)
Design by: Gordon Summers
Edge: 150 YEARS OF NURSING
Obverse: 2c

			UNC	BU	Proof
2010	6,175,000		£3.00	£7.50	£10.00
	25,000 max	Specimen in folder		£9.00	
	5,117 of 20k	.925 sterling silver proof			£30.00
	2,770 of 3,5k	.925 sterling silver Piedfort proof			£50.00
	472 of 1000	.917 gold proof			£550.00

COMMEMORATIVE TYPE 24
King James' Bible
KING JAMES BIBLE | 1611 - 2011
(400 years anniversay - King James' Bible)
Design by: Paul Stafford & Benjamin Wright
Edge: THE AUTHORISED VERSION
Obverse: 2b

			Used	BU	Proof
2011	975,000		£4.00	£10.00	£15.00
	25,000 max	Specimen in folder		£20.00	
	4,494 of 20k	.925 sterling silver proof			£3500
	2,394 of 3,5k	.925 sterling silver Piedfort proof			£70.00
	355 of 1000	.917 gold proof			£700.00

COMMEMORATIVE TYPE 25
Mary Rose
THE MARY ROSE | TWO POUNDS
(500 Years - Mary Rose)
Design by: John Bergdahl
Edge: 1511 . YOUR NOBLEST SHIPPE .
Obverse: 2c

			Used	BU	Proof
2011	1,040,000		£4.00	£10.00	£15.00
	25,000 max	Specimen in folder		£20.00	
	6,618 of 20k	.925 sterling silver proof			£40.00
	2,680 of ?2k	.925 sterling silver Piedfort proof			£60.00
	692 of 1000	.917 gold proof			£600.00

COMMEMORATIVE TYPE 26
Olympic Handover
LONDON 2012 | RIO 2016
(Olympic handover ceremony)
Design by: Jonathan Olliffe
Edge: I CALL UPON THE YOUTH OF THE WORLD
Obverse: 2d

			Used	BU	Proof
2012	845,000		£4.00	£10.00	£15.00
		Specimen in folder		£25.00	
	12,000 max	.925 sterling silver proof			£90.00
	2000 max	.925 sterling silver Piedfort proof			£150.00
	100 max	.917 gold proof, price new			£1195.00

COMMEMORATIVE TYPE 27
Charles Dickens
1812 CHARLES DICKENS 1870
(200th anniversary - birth of Charles Dickens)
Design by: Matthew Dent
Edge: SOMETHING WILL TURN UP
Obverse: 2d

			UNC	BU	Proof
2012	3,903,000		£3.00	£7.50	£10.00
		Specimen in folder		£10.00	
	20,000 max	.925 sterling silver proof			£45.00
	2000 max	.925 sterling silver Piedfort proof			£60.00
	850 max	.917 gold proof, price new			£900.00

28.40 mm • 12.0 grammes • bi-metal • various edge

COMMEMORATIVE TYPE 28
Underground Roundal
1863 | UNDERGROUND | 2013
(150th anniversary - The London Underground)
Design by: Edwina Ellis
Edge: MIND THE GAP
Obverse: 2b

			UNC	BU	Proof
2013	1,560,000		£3.00	£10.00	£15.00
		Specimen in folder		£20.00	
	7,500 max	.925 sterling silver proof			£40.00
	2,500 max	.925 sterling silver Piedfort proof, price new			£100.00
	750 max	.917 gold proof, price new			£750.00

COMMEMORATIVE TYPE 29
Underground Train
1863 | LONDON UNDERGROUND | 2013
(150th anniversary - The London Underground)
Design by: Edward Barber and Jay Osgerby
Edge: A pattern of circles connected by lines.
Obverse: 2b

			UNC	BU	Proof
2013	1,690,000		£3.00	£10.00	£15.00
		Specimen in folder		£20.00	
	7,500 max	.925 sterling silver proof			£40.00
	2,500 max	.925 sterling silver Piedfort proof, price new			£100.00
	750 max	.917 gold proof, price new			£750.00

COMMEMORATIVE TYPE 30
Spade Guinea
ANIVERSARY OF THE GOLDEN GUINEA | 2013
(350th anniversary - the Guinea)
Design by: Anthony Smith
Edge: WHAT IS A GUINEA? 'TIS A SPLENDID THING
Obverse: 2b

			UNC	BU	Proof
2013	2,990,000		£3.00	£10.00	£15.00
		Specimen in folder		£20.00	
	12,000 max?	.925 sterling silver proof, price new			£50.00
	4,013 max?	.925 sterling silver Piedfort proof, price new			£100.00
	1100 max?	.917 gold proof, price new			£900.00

COMMEMORATIVE TYPE 31
Design from Kitchener recruitment poster
THE FIRST WORLD WAR 1914 - 1918 | 2014
(Centenary - Start of WWI)
Design by: John Bergdahl
Edge: THE LAMPS ARE GOING OUT ALL OVER EUROPE
Obverse: 2b

		UNC	BU	Proof
2014		£3.00	£10.00	£15.00
	Specimen in folder, price new		£10.00	
8,014 max	.925 sterling silver proof, price new			£50.00
4,514 max	.925 sterling silver Piedfort proof, price new			£100.00
825 max	.917 gold proof, price new			£750.00

COMMEMORATIVE TYPE 32
Top of a Lighthouse
1514 TRINITY HOUSE 2014 | TWO POUNDS
(500 years of Trinity house)
Design by: Joe Whitlock Blundell and David Eccles
Edge: SERVING THE MARINER
Obverse 2

		UNC	BU	Proof
2014		£3.00	£10.00	£15.00
	Specimen in folder, price new		£10.00	
4,717 max	.925 sterling silver proof, price new			£50.00
3,514 max	.925 sterling silver Piedfort proof, price new			£100.00
375 max	.917 gold proof, price new			£750.00

COMMEMORATIVE TYPE 33
Royal Navy Battleship
THE FIRST WORLD WAR 1914 - 1918 | 2015
(Centenary - WWI, Royal Navy themed coin)
Design by: David Rowlands
Edge: THE SURE SHIELD OF BRITAIN
Obverse 2b

		UNC	BU	Proof
2015		£3.00	£10.00	£15.00
	Specimen in folder, price new		£10.00	
8,500 max	.925 sterling silver proof, price new			£50.00
4,000 max	.925 sterling silver Piedfort proof, price new			£100.00
900 max	.917 gold proof, price new			£750.00

| 28.40 mm • 12.0 grammes • bi-metal • various edge |

COMMEMORATIVE TYPE 34
King John & two noblemen
MAGNA CARTA | 1215 - 2015
(King John signing the Magna Carta)
Design by: John Bergdahl
Edge: FOUNDATION OF LIBERTY
Obverse 2d

	UNC	BU	Proof
2015	£3.00	£10.00	£15.00
Specimen in folder, price new		£10.00	
.925 sterling silver proof, exists?			TBC
.925 sterling silver Piedfort proof, exists?			TBC
.917 gold proof, exists?			TBC

What's currently legal tender?

All £5 coins are legal tender. Look out for non UK £5 coins being offered for face value as these are often from smaller provinces/islands and are therefore not legal tender in the United Kingdom. Particularly worrying are the coins from Tristan da Cunha, a tiny island group with a population of less than 300. So-called £5 coins from Tristan da Cunha often look very British but simply have TDC in the legend. Also, earlier crown coins should not be confused with these post-1990 £5 crowns. The crowns struck from 1972 to 1981 have a face value of 25p.

Which are hard to find?

All of these large coins are hard to find in circulation because they tend to get hoarded by the public when they are new and they are also made in lower numbers than the lower denominations. They are also heavy and not really practical to carry around for day-to-day transactions. The COMMEMORATIVE TYPE 7 with the 2000 date on the obverse seems scarcer than the 1999 dated millenium coin.

COMMEMORATIVE TYPE 1
Standard portrait of QE II
Design by: Raphael Maklouf
Double "E" monogram,
crowned
Design by: Leslie Durbin

			UNC	BU	Proof
1990	2,761,431		£6.00	£7.00	£10.00
	Specimen in card/folder			£10.00	
	56,102	.925 sterling silver proof			£25.00
	2,750	.917 gold proof			£1300.00

COMMEMORATIVE TYPE 2
Mary Gillick portrait of QEII
design by: Robert Elderton
St. Edward's crown
Design by: Robert Elderton

			UNC	BU	Proof
1993	1,834,655		£6.00	£7.00	£10.00
	Specimen in folder			£9.00	
	75,000	.925 sterling silver proof			£25.00
	2,750	.917 gold proof			£1200.00

COMMEMORATIVE TYPE 3
Standard portrait of QE II
Design by: Raphael Maklouf
Windsor Castle and Pennants
Design by: Avril Vaughan
Edge:
VIVAT REGINA ELIZABETHA

			UNC	BU	Proof
1996	2,396,100		£6.00	£7.00	£10.00
		Specimen in folder		£9.00	
	75,000	.925 sterling silver proof			£25.00
	2,750	.917 gold proof			£1200.00

COMMEMORATIVE TYPE 4
Conjoined busts of Elizabeth II
and Prince Philip
Design by: Philip Nathan
Arms of the Royal Couple,
crown, anchor. Design by: Leslie
Durbin

			UNC	BU	Proof
1997	1,733,000		£6.00	£7.00	£10.00
		Specimen in folder		£9.00	
	33,689	.925 sterling silver proof			£25.00
	2,750	.917 gold proof			£1200.00

COMMEMORATIVE TYPE 5
Standard portrait of QE II
Design by: Ian Rank-Broadley
Prince Charles, "The Prince's Tru:
Design by: Michael Noakes

			UNC	BU	Proof
1998	1,407,300	100,000	£5.50	£7.00	£10.00
		Specimen in folder		£9.00	
	35,000	.925 sterling silver proof			£25.00
	2,000	.917 gold proof			£1200.00

COMMEMORATIVE TYPE 6
Standard portrait of QEII
Design by: Ian Rank-Broadley
Portrait of Princess Diana
Design by: David Cornell

		UNC	BU	Proof
1999		£5.50	£7.00	£10.00
	Specimen in folder		£9.00	
49,545	.925 sterling silver proof			£25.00
2,750	.917 gold proof			£1200.00

COMMEMORATIVE TYPE 7
Standard portrait of QE II
(Dated either 1999 or 2000)
Design by: Ian Rank-Broadley
Clock at midnight, with map of British Isles
Design by: Jeffrey Matthews
Edge:
WHAT'S PAST IS PROLOGUE

		UNC	BU	Proof
Dated 1999 on Obverse		£5.50	£7.00	£10.00
	Specimen in folder		£9.00	
75,000	.925 sterling silver cased proof			£25.00
2,750	.917 gold cased proof			£1200.00
Dated 2000 on Obverse (not shown)		£10.00	£15.00	£15.00
	Specimen in folder		£15.00	
75,000	.925 sterling silver proof			£40.00
2,750	.917 gold proof			£1200.00

COMMEMORATIVE TYPE 7a

As above, with special dome mintmark, available only at the Millennium Dome.

2000	Specimen in folder	£30.00

COMMEMORATIVE TYPE 8
Standard portrait of QE II
Design by: Ian Rank-Broadley
Portrait of the Queen Mother
Design by: Ian Rank-Broadley

		UNC	BU	Proof
2000		£5.50	£7.00	£10.00
	Specimen in folder		£9.00	
100,000	.925 sterling silver proof			£30.00
14,850	.925 sterling silver Piedfort proof			£65.00
2,750	.917 gold proof			£1200.00

COMMEMORATIVE TYPE 9
Standard portrait of QEII
Design by: Ian Rank-Broadley
Wyon portrait of Victoria
Design by: Mary Milner Dickens

		UNC	BU	Proof
2001	851,491	£6.00	£8.00	£10.00
	44,090	Specimen in folder		£11.00
19,812	.925 sterling silver proof			£30.00
2,831	.917 gold proof			£1200.00

COMMEMORATIVE TYPE 10
Queen Elizabeth II on horseback
Design by: Ian Rank-Broadley
Queen wearing robes and diadem
Design by: Ian Rank-Broadley

		UNC	BU	Proof
2002		£5.50	£7.00	£10.00
340,230	Specimen in folder		£9.00	
54,012	.925 sterling silver proof			£30.00
3,461	.917 gold proof			£1200.00

COMMEMORATIVE TYPE 11
Standard portrait of QEII
Design by: Ian Rank-Broadley
Portrait of Queen Mother
Design by: Avril Vaughan.
**Edge: STRENGTH DIGNITY
LAUGHTER**

		UNC	BU	Proof
2002		£5.50	£7.00	£10.00
	Specimen in folder		£9.00	
35,000	.925 sterling silver proof			£30.00
2,750	.917 gold proof			£1200.00

COMMEMORATIVE TYPE 12
Sketched portrait of QE II
Design by: Tom Philips
"GOD SAVE THE QUEEN"
Design by: Tom Philips

		UNC	BU	Proof
2003	1,307,010	£5.50	£7.00	£10.00
	Specimen in folder		£9.00	
75,000	.925 sterling silver proof			£30.00
3,500	.917 gold proof			£1200.00

COMMEMORATIVE TYPE 13
Standard portrait of QEII
Design by: Ian Rank-Broadley
Conjoined Britannia and Marianne
Design by: David Gentlemen

			UNC	BU	Proof
2004	1,205,594		£6.00	£8.00	£10.00
	11, 295 of 15k	.925 sterling silver proof			£30.00
	2,500	.925 sterling silver piedfort proof			£120.00
	926 of 1,500	.917 gold proof			£1200.00
	501	.9995 platinum cased proof (3.0271 troy oz)			£3,800.00

COMMEMORATIVE TYPE 14
Standard portrait of QE II
design by: Ian Rank-Broadley
Portrait of Horatio Nelson
design by: James Butler
Edge: ENGLAND EXPECTS
EVERYMAN TO DO HIS DUTY

			UNC	BU	Proo
2005	1,075,516 inc. Type 15		£5.50	£7.00	£10.00
	72,498	Specimen in folder		£11.00	
	12,852	.925 sterling silver proof			£30.00
	1,760	.917 gold proof			£1200.00

COMMEMORATIVE TYPE 15
Standard portrait of QEII
design by: Ian Rank-Broadley
HMS Victory & Temeraire
design by: Clive Duncan

			UNC	BU	Proo
2005	Inc. above, with Type 14		£5.50	£7.00	£10.00
	79,868	Specimen in folder		£11.00	
	Specimen set (contains both 2005 folders, in sleeve)			£25.00	
	21,448	.925 sterling silver proof			£30.00
	1,805	.917 gold proof			£1200.00

COMMEMORATIVE TYPE 16
Standard portrait of QEII
Design by: Ian Rank-Broadley
Ceremonial Trumpets
with Banners
Design by:
Danuta Solowiej-Wedderburn
Edge: DUTY SERVICE FAITH

			UNC	BU	Proof
2006			£5.50	£7.00	£10.00
	330,790	Specimen in folder		£9.00	
	20,790 of 50k	.925 sterling silver proof			£30.00
	5,000	.925 sterling silver piedfort proof			£80.00
	2,750	.917 gold proof			£1200.00

COMMEMORATIVE TYPE 17
Standard portrait of QEII
Design by: Ian Rank-Broadley
The North Rose Window at
Westminster Abbey
Design by: Emma Noble
Edge: MY STRENGTH AND STAY

			UNC	BU	Proof
2007	2,396,100		£5.50	£7.00	£10.00
	260,856	Specimen in folder		£10.00	
	15,186 of 35k	.925 sterling silver proof			£40.00
	2,000 of 5,000	.925 sterling silver piedfort proof			£80.00
	2,380 of 2,500	.917 gold proof			£1200.00
	250	Platinum piedfort proof			£4000.00

COMMEMORATIVE TYPE 18
Standard portrait of QEII
Design by: Ian Rank-Broadley
Portrait of Elizabeth I
Westminster Abbey
Design by: Rod Kelly
Edge: I HAVE REIGNED WITH YOUR LOVES

		UNC	BU	Proof
2008		£5.50	£7.00	£10.00
	Specimen in folder		£10.00	
9,216 of 20k	.925 sterling silver proof			£40.00
1,602 of 2k	.925 sterling silver piedfort proof			£80.00
1,500	.917 gold proof			£1200.00
125 of 150	Platinum piedfort proof			£4000.00

COMMEMORATIVE TYPE 19
Standard portrait of QEII
Design by: Ian Rank-Broadley
Portrait of the Price of Wales
Design by: Ian Rank-Broadley
Edge: SIXTIETH BIRTHDAY

		UNC	BU	Proof
2008	30,649	£5.50	£7.00	£10.00
	54,746	Specimen in folder	£10.00	
6,264	.925 sterling silver proof			£40.00
1088 of 5k	.925 sterling silver piedfort proof			£80.00
867 of 1500	.917 gold proof			£1200.00
54 of 150	Platinum piedfort proof			£4000.00

COMMEMORATIVE TYPE 20
Standard portrait of QEII
Design by: Ian Rank-Broadley
Henry VIII
Design by: John Bergdahl

		UNC	BU	Proof
2009		£5.50	£7.00	£10.00
	Specimen in folder		£10.00	
10,419 of 20k	.925 sterling silver proof			£40.00
3,580 of 4009	.925 sterling silver piedfort proof			£80.00
1130 of 1509	.917 gold proof			£1200.00
100	Platinum piedfort proof			£4000.00

COMMEMORATIVE TYPE 21
Standard portrait of QEII
Design by: Ian Rank-Broadley
Countdown '3'
Design by: Claire Aldridge

		UNC	BU	Proof
2009		£5.50	£7.00	£10.00
	Specimen in folder		£10.00	
26,645 of 30k	.925 sterling silver proof			£40.00
4,874 of 6k	.925 sterling silver piedfort proof			£80.00
1860 of 4000	.917 gold proof			£1200.00

Celebration of Britain: Mind, Body and Spirit 2009 - 2010.

CAUTION: Chinese made forgeries of this series exist. The fakes have inconsistently frosted details and poorly executed colouring of the '2012' logos.

The Royal Mint issued a whopping eighteen different crowns in conjunction with the London 2012 Olympics, eight of which are shown on the following pages. Starting in June 2009, one was issued every twenty-eight days until late 2010. The eighteen coins were made available as a complete set as well as being available in groups of six (themed: 'Mind', 'Body' and 'Spirit').

They were all struck as sterling silver proofs. Two of them: the London (15) and Churchill (16) coins were also struck in cupro-nickel. The obverse design is the same as that used for COMMEMORA-TIVE TYPE 24, but dated either 2009 or 2010, as indicated. The reverse designs are all of a high standard and by Shane Greeves. Each design is accompanied by some wise words with very loose connections to the subject matter of the designs featured. I can only assume they are offered as guidance and inspiration!

CELEBRATION TYPE 1
Mind Series (with green London 2012 logo)
Clock-face of the Palace of Westminster
Walter Bagehot quote:
"Nations touch at their summits"

2009   .925 Sterling silver proof   £25-£40

CELEBRATION TYPE 2
Mind Series (with green London 2012 logo)
Stonehenge
William Blake quote:
"Great things are done when men and mountains meet"

2009   .925 Sterling silver proof   £25-£40

CELEBRATION TYPE 2
Mind Series (with green London 2012 logo)
The Angel of the North
William Shakespeare quote:
"I have touched the highest point of all my greatness"

2009   .925 Sterling silver proof   £25-£40

CELEBRATION TYPE 4
Mind Series (with green London 2012 logo)
The Flying Scotsman
William Shakespeare quote:
"True hope is swift"

2009   .925 Sterling silver proof   £25-£40

CELEBRATION TYPE 5
Mind Series (with green London 2012 logo)
Sculpture of Isaac Newton
William Shakespeare quote:
"Make not your thoughts your prisons"

2009   .925 Sterling silver proof   £25-£40

CELEBRATION TYPE 6
Mind Series (with green London 2012 logo)
The Globe Theatre
William Shakespeare quote:
"We are such stuff as dreams are made of"

2009   .925 Sterling silver proof   £25-£40

CELEBRATION TYPE 7
Body Series (with red London 2012 logo)
Rhossili Bay
William Blake quote:
"To see a world in a grain of sand"

2010   .925 Sterling silver proof   £25-£40

CELEBRATION TYPE 8
Body Series (with red London 2012 logo)
Giant's Causeway
Alice Oswald quote:
"When the stone began to dream"

2010   .925 Sterling silver proof   £25-£40

Celebration of Britain: Mind, Body and Spirit 2009 - 2010 (continued).

CELEBRATION TYPE 9
Body Series (with red London 2012 logo)
The River Thames
Percy Bysshe Shelley quote:
"Tameless, and swift, and proud"

2010   .925 Sterling silver proof   £25-£40

CELEBRATION TYPE 10
Body Series (with red London 2012 logo)
Barn Owl
Samuel Johnson quote:
"The natural flights of the human mind"

2010   .925 Sterling silver proof   £25-£40

CELEBRATION TYPE 11
Body Series (with red London 2012 logo)
Oak leaves and an acorn
Alfred, Lord Tennyson quote:
"To strive, to seek ... and not to yield"

2010   .925 Sterling silver proof   £25-£40

CELEBRATION TYPE 12
Body Series (with red London 2012 logo)
Weather-vane
Charlotte Brontë quote:
"Never may a cloud come o'er the sunshine of your mind"

2010   .925 Sterling silver proof   £25-£40

CELEBRATION TYPE 13
Spirit Series (with blue London 2012 logo)
Floral emblems of the UK
John Lennon quote:
"And the world will be as one"

2010   .925 Sterling silver proof   £25-£40

CELEBRATION TYPE 14
Spirit Series (with blue London 2012 logo)
White rabbit from Alice in Wonderland
T S Elliot quote:
"All touched by a common genius"

2010	.925 Sterling silver proof	£25-£40

CELEBRATION TYPE 15
Spirit Series (with blue London 2012 logo)
View down the Mall, London
Alfred, Lord Tennyson quote:
"Kind hearts are more than coronets"

2010	.925 Sterling silver proof	£25-£40
2010	Cupro-Nickel proof	£10-£20

CELEBRATION TYPE 16
Spirit Series (with blue London 2012 logo)
Winston Churchill Statue
Anita Roddick quote:
"Be daring, be first, be different, be just"

2010	.925 Sterling silver proof	£25-£40
2010	Cupro-Nickel proof	£10-£20

CELEBRATION TYPE 17
Spirit Series (with blue London 2012 logo)
Musical intsruments sculpture
Lennon & McCartney quote:
"All you need is love"

2010	.925 Sterling silver proof	£25-£40

CELEBRATION TYPE 18
Spirit Series (with blue London 2012 logo)
Image of campaigner Equiano
William Shakespeare quote:
"To thine own self be true"

2010	.925 Sterling silver proof	£25-£40

COMMEMORATIVE TYPE 22
Standard portrait of QEII
Design by: Ian Rank-Broadley
1660 Restoration of Monarchy
Design by: David Cornell
Obverse: Type as no. 20

		UNC	BU	Proof
2010		£5.50	£7.00	£10.00
	Specimen in folder		£10.00	
6,518 of 20k	.925 sterling silver proof			£40.00
4,435 of 5k	.925 sterling silver piedfort proof			£80.00
1,182 of 1,200	.917 gold proof			£1200.00
100 max	Platinum piedfort proof			£?

COMMEMORATIVE TYPE 23
Standard portrait of QEII
Design by: Ian Rank-Broadley
Countdown '2'
Design by: Claire Aldridge

		UNC	BU	Proof
2010		£5.50	£7.00	£10.00
	Specimen in folder		£10.00	
20,159 of 30k	.925 sterling silver proof			£40.00
4,435	.925 sterling silver piedfort proof			£80.00
1,562 of 3k	.917 gold proof			£1200.00

As part of the Royal Mints unprecedented drive to make as many themed coins as possible, higher face value coins were also issued. In silver: a £10 with a diameter of 65mm and weight of 5oz (155.5g) featuring the winged horse pegasus. A £500 with a diameter of 100mm and weight of one kilogram, featuring the stylised words 'XXX OLYMPIAD'.

Gold olympic themed coins coins consisted of 6x £25 coins (2 each for 'faster', 'higher' and 'stronger'), 3x £100 coins (one each for 'faster', 'higher' and 'stronger') and a crude looking one kilogram gold coin with a face value of £1000.

COMMEMORATIVE TYPE 24
Standard portrait of QEII
Design by: Ian Rank-Broadley
Royal Wedding of William &
Catherine
Design by: Mark Richards

		UNC	BU	Proof
2011	?	£7.00	£9.00	
	250,000	Specimen in folder	£20.00	
	26,069 of 50k	.925 sterling silver proof / or 3000 max gold plated coin		£40.00
	3000 max	.925 sterling silver piedfort proof		£80.00
	2,066 of 3k	.917 gold proof		£1200.00
	133 of 200	Platinum piedfort proof		£4000.00

COMMEMORATIVE TYPE 25
Standard portrait of QEII
Design by: Ian Rank-Broadley
Countdown '1'
Design by: Claire Aldridge

		UNC	BU	Proof
2011		£6.00	£7.00	£10.00
		Specimen in folder	£10.00	
	25,877 of 30k	.925 sterling silver proof		£40.00
	4000	.925 sterling silver piedfort proof		£80.00
	1,300 of 3k	.917 gold proof		£1200.00

COMMEMORATIVE TYPE 26
Standard portrait of QEII
Design by: Ian Rank-Broadley
Prince Philip 90th Birthday
Design by: Mark Richards

		UNC	BU	Proof
2011		£5.50	£7.00	£10.00
	Specimen in folder		£10.00	
4,599 of 20k	.925 sterling silver proof			£40.00
2,659 of 4k	.925 sterling silver piedfort proof			£80.00
636 of 1,200	.917 gold proof			£1200.00
49 of 90	Platinum piedfort proof			£4000.00

COMMEMORATIVE TYPE 27
Standard portrait of QEII
Design by: Ian Rank-Broadley
Countdown 'O'
Design by: Claire Aldridge

		UNC	BU	Proof
2012		£5.50	£7.00	£10.00
	Specimen in folder / card		£10.00	
30,000 max	.925 sterling silver proof			£40.00
4000 max	.925 sterling silver piedfort proof			£80.00
3000 max	.917 gold proof			£1200.00

COMMEMORATIVE TYPE 28
Standard portrait of QEII
Design by: Ian Rank-Broadley
London 2012 Olympics
Commemorative
Design by: Siaman Miah
Obverse: Type as no. 24

		UNC	BU	Proof
2012		£7.00	£9.00	
	Specimen in folder		£10.00	
100,000 max	.925 sterling silver proof			£30.00
7,000 max	.925 sterling silver piedfort proof			£100.00
12,500 max	.925 sterling silver, gold plating*			?
5000 max	.917 gold proof			£2500.00

COMMEMORATIVE TYPE 29
Standard portrait of QEII
Design by: Ian Rank-Broadley
London 2012 Paralympics
Commemorative
Design by: Pippa Sanderson
Obverse: Type as no. 24

		UNC	BU	Proof
2012		£5.50	£7.00	
	Specimen in folder		£10.00	
10,000/3,000	.925 sterling silver proof / or gold plated version			£40.00
2012 max	.925 sterling silver piedfort proof			£100.00
5000 max	.917 gold proof			£2500.00

97

COMMEMORATIVE TYPE 30
Special portrait of QEII
Design by: Ian Rank-Broadley
Queen's Diamond Jubilee
Design by: Ian Rank-Broadley

		UNC	BU	Proof
2012		£5.50	£7.00	£10.00
	Specimen in folder		£10.00	
75,000 max	.925 sterling silver proof			£40.00
3,250 max	.925 sterling silver piedfort proof			£100.00
12,500 max	.925 sterling silver, gold plated*			?
3850 max	.917 gold proof			£2000.00
250 max	Platinum piedfort proof			£5000.00

To mark the Jubilee there was also a £10 coin (as silver or gold proof) with a diameter of 65mm - these have the same obverse as above and feature the queen enthroned and facing on the reverse. Prices new were about £450 for the silver version and £9,500 for the gold coin. One kilogram silver (£500) and one kilogram gold (£1000) coins were also made to mark the Queens jubilee. Both use the same obverse as above and show the full Royal Arms on the reverse.

COMMEMORATIVE TYPE 31
Standard portrait of QEII
Design by: Ian Rank-Broadley
Anniversary of Coronation
Design by: Emma Noble
Obverse: Type as no. 24

		UNC	BU	Proof
2013		£5.50	£7.00	£10.00
	Specimen in folder		£10.00	
15,000 max	.925 sterling silver proof			£70.00
3,250 max	.925 sterling silver piedfort proof, price new			£160.00
12,500 max	.925 sterling silver, gold plated*			?
2,000 max	.917 gold proof, price new			£1800.00
100 max	Platinum piedfort proof, price new			£6400.00

*Previously, the gold plating of silver coins was exclusively the reserve of dubious eBay sellers or private makers of coins in order to somehow justify the extortionate asking prices. It's not particularly hard to do, and I fail to see how a micro-thin layer of gold can add any value to a silver coin. I was shocked when I discovered that the Royal Mint had also taken the decision to make and sell gold plated silver coins.

COMMEMORATIVE TYPE 32
Standard portrait of QEII
Design by: Ian Rank-Broadley
Christening of Prince George
Design by: John Bergdahl

		UNC	BU	Proof
2013		£8.00	£10.00	
	Specimen in folder		£13.00	
75,000 max	.925 sterling silver proof			£70.00
2,500 max?	.925 sterling silver piedfort proof			£100.00
1000 max?	.917 gold proof			£2000.00
100 max?	Platinum piedfort proof			?
St. George Rev	Initially a St.George proof version was issued*			£80.00

*Shortly after the birth of Prince George, a silver proof only £5 Crown was released with the Pistrucci St. George Reverse. This was the first coin that the Royal Mint suddenly refused to sell to other businesses, offering it exclusively to their private customers for £80.

Note that for both the 2013 coronation (no. 31) and Prince George (no.32) one kilo versions with a face value of £500 were struck in silver. These are both available new for £2600. A gold kilo version of no. 32 is currently available for £50,000!

COMMEMORATIVE TYPE 33
Standard portrait of QEII
Design by: Ian Rank-Broadley
300th Anniversary of the Death of Queen Anne
Design by: Mark Richards
Obverse: Type as no. 24

		UNC	BU	Proof
2014		£7.00	£9.00	
	Specimen in folder, price new		£13.00	
3100 max	.925 sterling silver proof, price new			£75.00
1665 max	.925 sterling silver, gold plated			?
(was 2014 max)4028 max	.925 sterling silver piedfort proof, price new			£160.00
375 max	.917 gold proof, price new			£1,800.00
250 max?	Platinum piedfort proof			?

2014: 'The Portrait of Britain Collection' is a set of four Five Pound coins. See page 103.

38.61 mm • 28.28 grammes • cupro-nickel • edge: milled

COMMEMORATIVE TYPE 34
Standard portrait of QEII
Design by: Ian Rank-Broadley
Winston Churchill -
50th Anniversary of his death
Design by: Mark Richards
Obverse: Type as no. 24
Edge (on proofs): NEVER
FLINCH, NEVER WEARY, NEVER
DESPAIR

		UNC	BU	Proof
2015		£8.00	£10.00	
	Specimen in folder		£13.00	
7,500 max	.925 sterling silver proof, price new			£80.00
2,000 max	.925 sterling silver piedfort proof, price new			£160.00
?	.925 sterling silver, gold plated			?
620 max	.917 gold proof, price new			£1800.00
65 max	Platinum piedfort proof, price new			£5000.00

COMMEMORATIVE TYPE 35
Standard portrait of QEII
Design by: Ian Rank-Broadley
Battle of Waterloo -
200th Anniversary
Design by: David lawrence
Obverse: Type as no. 24
Edge (on proofs): THE NEAREST
RUN THING YOU EVER SAW

		UNC	BU	Proof
2015		£7.00	£9.00	
	Specimen in folder, new price		£13.00	
?	.925 sterling silver proof			TBC
?	.925 sterling silver piedfort proof			TBC
?	.925 sterling silver, gold plated			TBC
?	.917 gold proof			TBC
?	Platinum piedfort proof			TBC

The £20 Coin

A new £20 silver coin was issued in 2013. To date they all feature the Rank-Broadly portrait of the Queen on the obverse. The 2013 coin has the Pistrucci St. George on the reverse. The 2014 £20 coin shows Britannia with a lion on the reverse and the 2015 coin features Winston Churchill.

They are offered by the Royal Mint for £20.00 plus postage. The value of the silver content is about £5.66 which is much lower, but nothing unusual as the face value of circulating coins has been less than the material value contained within for centuries. What confuses me though, is the legal tender status of the coin. The Royal Mint web site itself made no mention of a £20 coin being legal tender until early in January 2014 when it was added to their list of legal tender coins (coins with £10 and £25 face value are still not shown). I'm no legal expert, but as far as I can tell the 'Coinage Act 1971' has not been amended since 2011 (which was a fairly minor change) and it makes no mention of a £20 being legal tender. Perhaps it will be amended in the future.

There have certainly been some issues with the acceptance of the coins at face value, not only in shops but also at banks and post offices.

2013 St. George reverse

2013 & 2014 obverse

2014 WWI '1914 1918' reverse

The 2015 Churchill coin doesn't have a date on the reverse like the others. Instead, the date is featured on the obverse and the 'TWENTY POUNDS' is abbreviated to '20 POUNDS'.

2015 Churchill reverse

		BU in pack
2013	St. George reverse	£28.00
2014	WWI 1914 1918 Britannia reverse	£28.00
2015	Winston Churchill reverse	£30.00

The £100 Coin

Following the success of the £20 coin, the Royal Mint made and sold its first £100 coin in 2015. 50,000 of these were sold by the Royal Mint for £100 each. Currently the silver value is about £22.60 and again, I'm not entirely clear on the true legal tender status of this coins (see also notes for the previous silver £20 coins). After they sold out at the Royal Mint the were being sold on eBay and other online outlets for up to £200! Since then the values have come down and seem to have stabilised.

2015 £100 Coin
Standard portrait of QEII with '100 POUNDS 2015'
Design by: Ian Rank-Broadley
'Big Ben' as seen from below
Design by: Glyn Davies and Laura Clancy

BU

2015	50,000	Specimen in folder	£130-£150

The Portrait of Britain Collection

Yet another special set of coins. I personally don't collect any Royal Mint modern coins, but I do sometimes wonder how people that do collect them manage to keep up with all the new commemorative issues, special sets, bullion coins and new denominations of the last few years! I also feel that being financially able to collect all of the Royal Mint new issue coins must be outside the realms of possibility for a lot of collectors now, which is a shame.

This set celebrates four world renowned landmarks of Britain (that all happen to be in London), namely Big Ben, Buckingham Palace, Tower Bridge and Trafalgar Square. The Big Ben coin is very similar to the £100 coin design, shown on the previous page.

Each reverse design is by Glyn Davies and Laura Clancy. I'm afraid I do not currently have pictures to show here.

BU

2014	5,000 max	Set of 4x .925 silver proofs, price new	£360.00

United Kingdom Banknotes

The UK currently has four denominations of legal tender banknotes in circulation; the £5, £10, £20 and £50 notes. Some banks in Scotland and in Northern Ireland also issue Sterling banknotes in the same denomination as the Bank of England types (plus the Royal Bank of Scotland continues to issue smaller numbers of £1 notes). These notes are not officially legal tender but they are of course readily accepted within the countries in which they circulate. All of the Scottish and Northern Irish banknotes have to be backed up by Bank of England money; in other words, a bank issuing notes in Scotland or Northern Ireland has to theoretically hold in its vaults the same amount of Bank of England money. Usually this Bank of England money is held in the form of special high-value banknotes that are exchanged just between banks. The circulating Scottish and Northern Ireland banknotes are not covered in this book (perhaps in a future edition).

The four current circulating Bank of England notes are: £5 - Mainly green with Elizabeth Fry on the reverse. £10 - Mainly orange with Charles Darwin on the reverse. £20 - Mainly purple with Adam Smith on the reverse. £50 - Mainly red with Matthew Boulton and James Watt on the reverse.

The 'promise to pay the bearer' on each Bank of England banknote never expires, even when the notes of that type have long since been removed from circulation. As a result, every single Bank of England note can always be redeemed for its face value at the Bank of England, and usually at any UK bank. Shopkeepers and other merchants are not obliged to accept older Bank of England notes. Before redeeming older Bank of England notes it's obviously a good idea to check that they don't have a collectable worth first. This can be done using the Rotographic publication "Collectors' Banknotes" which is published regularly and includes valuations for all Bank of England and HM Treasury issued banknotes.

Banknote condition

Just as with coins, condition plays a very important role where the values of banknotes are concerned. Most collectors will attempt to collect the banknotes in the best condition they can afford. With modern banknotes this will nearly always be uncirculated (mint condition) examples, as such examples of modern banknotes are usually obtainable. With this in mind, most well-used, tatty, creased and dirty banknotes that have exchanged hands many times are only likely to be worth their face value. EF is an abbreviation for Extremely Fine and means that a note is in very good condition, but just a little way from being classed as UNCirculated. VF means Very Fine and is quite a common grade for modern notes that have seen limited average use.

Serial numbers

Collectors like interesting serial numbers too. If you ever get given a note with a low serial number, where at least the first 3 digits of the 6 digit number are zeros, keep hold of it. A note with the serial number AH43 000954 will be slightly more interesting than AH43 874563, for example. The note AH43 000001 would of course be more interesting still. AA01 000045 would be even more desirable! Collectors also like interesting patterns in numbers, like AH43 434343, AH22 222222 or AH12 345678. You won't get offered huge amounts of money for notes with interesting serial numbers, but you might persuade someone to give you slightly more than face value, assuming the note is in good condition.

Banknote images are © Bank of England.

COLLECTORS' COINS - DECIMAL ISSUES OF THE UK

Signed by <u>Merlyn Lowther</u>, the chief cashier of the Bank of England from 1999 to 2003.

DETAILS	EF	UNC

Letter, Letter, Number, Number, followed by 6 digits

	EF	UNC
Number AA01 000000 Special Specimen note		£800.00
HA** followed by 6 digits (special first run)	£6.00	£14.00
HC01 followed by 6 digits (first prefix)	£25.00	£75.00
CL**, DL** or EL** then 6 digits (special column sort prefix)	£10.00	£20.00
XA** to XK** followed by 6 digits (varnish trial prefix)	£200.00	
LL** followed by 6 digits (replacement notes)	£10.00	£20.00
ER50 followed by 6 digits (special presentation pack issue)*		£25
HM02 followed by 6 digits (special presentation pack issue)*		£25
HM03 followed by 6 digits (special presentation pack issue)*		£25
QC03 followed by 6 digits (special presentation pack issue)*		£25
QC50 followed by 6 digits (special presentation pack issue)*		£25
JB** followed by 6 digits (last Lowther prefix)		£10.00

The first Elizabeth Fry £5 notes were withdrawn as the serial numbers were not properly varnished and could be partially rubbed off. Initially they were sought after and the extra demand meant they were worth slightly more. The affected notes were taken in, treated and then re released into circulation. None of the original issue now commands a premium.

* These notes were only issued as part of special sets.

Signed by <u>Andrew Bailey</u>, the chief cashier of the Bank of England from 2004 to 2011.

Letter, Letter, Number, Number, followed by 6 digits

	EF	UNC
JB** followed by 6 digits (first prefix run)		£10.00
EL02 followed by 6 digits (special column sort prefix)	£10.00	£25.00
EL** followed by 6 digits (special column sort prefix)	£6.00	£12.00
LL** followed by 6 digits (replacement notes)	£10.00	£20.00
LE** followed by 6 digits (last Bailey prefix)		£10.00

Signed by <u>Chris Salmon</u>, the chief cashier of the Bank of England from 2011 to date.

Letter, Letter, Number, Number, followed by 6 digits

	EF	UNC
LE** followed by 6 digits (first Salmon prefix)		£8.00
Later Salmon prefixes LJ** and MA** noted		£8.00

Signed by <u>Merlyn Lowther</u>, the chief cashier of the Bank of England from 1999 to 2003.

DETAILS	VF	EF	UNC
Letter, Letter, Number, Number, followed by 6 digits			
Number AA01 000000 Special Specimen note			£800.00
AA01 followed by 6 digits (first prefix)		£20.00	£50.00
AA01 followed by 6 digits (first prefix, worded 'and company')*¹		£30.00	£50.00
AD** followed by 6 digits (worded 'and company')*¹		£60.00	£120.00
AH80 followed by 6 digits (last prefix of first type)	£50.00	£150.00	£300.00
AJ01 followed by 6 digits (first production run)		£50.00	£100.00
EL** followed by 6 digits (special column sort prefix)			£20.00
LL** followed by 6 digits (replacement notes)		£75.00	£150.00
LL** followed by 6 digits (replacement notes 'and company')*		£40.00	£90.00
CC80 followed by 6 digits (highest prefix known*²)	£20.00	£75.00	£150.00
MH**, MJ**, MK**, MM** (experimental notes)	£100.00	£150.00	
ER50 followed by 6 digits (special presentation pack issue)*			£30.00
QC50 followed by 6 digits (special presentation pack issue)*			£30.00
QV10 followed by 6 digits (special presentation pack issue)*			£30.00
VR10 followed by 6 digits (special presentation pack issue)*			£30.00

* These notes were only issued as part of special sets.

*¹ These notes have the wording 'The Governor and Company of the Bank of England' in the band of text above the central oval where the Queen's watermark appears. A variety exists with the wording 'The Governor <u>and the</u> Company of the Bank of England'. Both types were made in high numbers.

*2 The CC** prefix overlaps with the CC** Bailey notes below. Until recently it was thought that CC40 was the last Lowther prefix. This is not that case as prefixes up to CC80 have been noted on newly issued Lowther notes.

Signed by <u>Andrew Bailey</u>, the chief cashier of the Bank of England from 2004 to 2011.

DETAILS	EF	UNC
Letter, Letter, Number, Number, followed by 6 digits		
CC41 followed by 6 digits (lowest known prefix)	£60.00	£120.00
EL** followed by 6 digits (special column sort prefix)	£15.00	£25.00
EL80 followed by 6 digits (last column sort EL prefix)	£50.00	£100.00
HL01 followed by 6 digits (first column sort HL prefix)	£50.00	£100.00
HL** followed by 6 digits (special column sort prefix)	£20.00	£50.00
LL** followed by 6 digits (replacement notes)	£15.00	£35.00
LA** followed by 6 digits (last Lowther prefix)	£15.00	£35.00

Signed by <u>Chris Salmon</u>, the chief cashier of the Bank of England from 2011 to date.

Letter, Letter, Number, Number, followed by 6 digits

Prefix JH** followed by 6 digits (first Salmon prefix)	£14.00
Later Salmon prefixes? Not current information	

Banknote images are © Bank of England.

Signed by <u>Andrew Bailey,</u> the chief cashier of the Bank of England from 2004 to 2011.

DETAILS	EF	UNC
Letter, Letter, Number, Number, followed by 6 digits		
AA01 followed by 6 digits (first Bailey prefix)	£25.00	£50.00
AL** followed by 6 digits (special column sort prefix)	£25.00	£40.00
LL** followed by 6 digits (replacement notes)	£30.00	£50.00
HD36 followed by 6 digits (last Bailey prefix)		£35.00

Signed by <u>Chris Salmon</u> the chief cashier of the Bank of England from 2011 to date.

Letter, Letter, Number, Number, followed by 6 digits

HA** followed by 6 digits (first Salmon prefix)		£28.00
Later Salmon prefixes, HJ** noted		£26.00

Signed by <u>Chris Salmon</u>, the chief cashier of the Bank of England from 2011 to date.

DETAILS   **UNC**

Letter, Number, Number, followed by 6 digits

AA** followed by 6 digits (first prefix)	£80.00
Later Salmon prefixes (noted to AJ**)	£75.00

Banknote images are © Bank of England.

From 1971 to 1982, The Royal Mint issued proof coin sets sealed in plastic, enclosed in lightweight card envelopes. Generally the sets on this page sell for between £6.00 and £15.00.

Year	Pieces	Coins	Notes
1971	6	½p, 1p, 2p, 5p, 10p, 50p	
1972	7	½p, 1p, 2p, 5p, 10p, 25p, 50p	Silver Wedding crown
1973	6	½p, 1p, 2p, 5p, 10p, 50p	
1974	6	½p, 1p, 2p, 5p, 10p, 50p	
1975	6	½p, 1p, 2p, 5p, 10p, 50p	
1976	6	½p, 1p, 2p, 5p, 10p, 50p	
1977	7	½p, 1p, 2p, 5p, 10p, 25p, 50p	Silver Jubilee crown
1978	6	½p, 1p, 2p, 5p, 10p, 50p	
1979	6	½p, 1p, 2p, 5p, 10p, 50p	
1980	6	½p, 1p, 2p, 5p, 10p, 50p	
1981	6	½p, 1p, 2p, 5p, 10p, 50p	
1982	7	½p, 1p, 2p, 5p, 10p, 20p, 50p	new 20p added

In 1983, the packaging was changed to a blue leatherette bookshelf type case.

Year	Pieces	Coins	Notes
1983	8	½p, 1p, 2p, 5p, 10p, 20p, 50p, £1	new £1 added
1984	8	½p, 1p, 2p, 5p, 10p, 20p, 50p, £1	

From 1985 onward, two types of packaging were offered: The "standard" blue leatherette case, and the "deluxe" red leather case. 1985 to 1999 sets are worth between £10.00 up to around £25.00.

Year	Pieces	Coins	Notes
1985	7	1p, 2p, 5p, 10p, 20p, 50p, £1	½p removed
1986	8	1p, 2p, 5p, 10p, 20p, 50p, £1, £2	Commonwealth Games
1987	7	1p, 2p, 5p, 10p, 20p, 50p, £1	
1988	7	1p, 2p, 5p, 10p, 20p, 50p, £1	
1989	9	1p, 2p, 5p, 10p, 20p, 50p, £1, £2, £2	Bill of Rights / Claim of Right
1990	8	1p, 2p, 5p, 5p, 10p, 20p, 50p, £1	Both 5p sizes
1991	7	1p, 2p, 5p, 10p, 20p, 50p, £1	
1992	9	1p, 2p, 5p, 10p, 10p, 20p, 50p, 50p, £1	Both 10p sizes; EEC 50p
1993	8	1p, 2p, 5p, 10p, 20p, 50p, £1, £5	Coronation Anniversary
1994	8	1p, 2p, 5p, 10p, 20p, 50p, £1, £2	Bank of England
1995	8	1p, 2p, 5p, 10p, 20p, 50p, £1, £2	Dove of Peace
1996	9	1p, 2p, 5p, 10p, 20p, 50p, £1, £2, £5	Football; 70th Birthday
1997	10	1p, 2p, 5p, 10p, 20p, 50p, 50p, £1, £2, £5	Both 50p's; Royal Wedding
1998	10	1p, 2p, 5p, 10p, 20p, 50p, 50p, £1, £2, £5	EU; Prince Charles
1999	9	1p, 2p, 5p, 10p, 20p, 50p, £1, £2, £5	Rugby, Princess Diana

From 2000 on, it is accepted that all sets will contain the standard 8 pieces: 1p, 2p, 5p, 10p, 20p, 50p, £1, and £2. The Royal Mint, also produce deluxe proof sets and executive proof sets, which contain the same coins but have better packaging. The deluxe and executive sets are often sold for a few pounds more than the standard sets. Sets dated 2000 to 2004 are worth around £30.00. Later sets are worth slightly more and usually the most recent are still available new for the Royal Mint retail price, which is currently around £60 - £100.

Recently 'Premium' sets have been introduced which include a medallion! And in 2013 the RM made the proof sets available in 'definitive' form, which include just the standard 1p to £2, a 'commemorative' set which is just the commemorative 50p, £1 and £2 coins and also a complete set made up of all the coins. I'm starting to lose track, and I honestly don't think the packaging will play much of a roll in the future - the coins are what they are, regardless of the current sales-packaging-strategy!

Year	Pieces	Commemorative issues
2000	10	50p Public Libraries, £5 Millennium
2001	10	£2 Marconi, £5 Victorian Era
2002	9	£5 Coronation Jubilee
2003	11	50p Women's Suffrage, £2 DNA, £5 Golden Jubilee
2004	10	50p Roger Bannister, £2 Trevithick's Steam Locomotive
2005	12	50p Johnson's Dictionary, £2 Guy Fawkes, £5 Nelson, £5 Trafalgar
2006	13	Both VC 50p's, Both Brunel £2's, £5 Queen's 80th Birthday
2007	12	50p Scouting, Union £2 and Slave Trade £2, Diamond Wedding £5
2008	11	Olypic Centenary £2, Charles £5, Elizabeth I £5
2009	12	Kew 50p, Darwin £2, Burns £2, Henry VIII £5
2010	13	Girl Guides 50p, London £1, Belfast £1, Nursing £2, Restoration £5
2011	14	WWF 50p, Edinburgh £1, Cardiff £1, Bible £2, Mary Rose £2, Philip £5
2012	10	Dickens £2, Accession £5
2013	15	Ironside 50p, Floral £1 x2, Underground £2 x2, Guinea £2, Coronation £5
2014	14	Games 50p, Floral £1 x2, WWI £2, Trinity £2, Queen Anne £5
2015	13	Battle of Britain 50p, Magna Carta £2, WWI £2, Churchill £5, Waterloo £5

In 1982, the Royal Mint introduced BU sets, which contain most of the coins contained in the Proof sets (crowns normally not included). These sets do not have the proof quality striking, and are packaged in a folder style, but they do provide history background text on the coins.

Year	Pieces	Coins	Notes
1982	7	¹/₂p, 1p, 2p, 5p, 10p, 20p, 50p	
1983	8	¹/₂p, 1p, 2p, 5p, 10p, 20p, 50p, £1	new £1 added
1984	8	¹/₂p, 1p, 2p, 5p, 10p, 20p, 50p, £1	
1985	7	1p, 2p, 5p, 10p, 20p, 50p, £1	¹/₂p removed
1986	8	1p, 2p, 5p, 10p, 20p, 50p, £1, £2	Commonwealth Games
1987	7	1p, 2p, 5p, 10p, 20p, 50p, £1	
1988	7	1p, 2p, 5p, 10p, 20p, 50p, £1	
1989	7	1p, 2p, 5p, 10p, 20p, 50p, £1	
1990	8	1p, 2p, 5p, 5p, 10p, 20p, 50p, £1	lg & sm 5p
1991	7	1p, 2p, 5p, 10p, 20p, 50p, £1	
1992	9	1p, 2p, 5p, 10p, 10p, 20p, 50p, 50p, £1	lg & sm 10p; EEC
1993	8	1p, 2p, 5p, 10p, 20p, 50p, £1, £5	Coronation Anniversary
1994	8	1p, 2p, 5p, 10p, 20p, 50p, £1, £2	Bank of England
1995	8	1p, 2p, 5p, 10p, 20p, 50p, £1, £2	Dove of Peace
1996	8	1p, 2p, 5p, 10p, 20p, 50p, £1, £2	Football
1997	9	1p, 2p, 5p, 10p, 20p, 50p, 50p, £1, £2	lg & sm 50p
1998	9	1p, 2p, 5p, 10p, 20p, 50p, 50p, £1, £2	EU
1999	8	1p, 2p, 5p, 10p, 20p, 50p, £1, £2	Rugby
2000	9	1p, 2p, 5p, 10p, 20p, 50p, 50p, £1, £2	Public Libraries
2001	9	1p, 2p, 5p, 10p, 20p, 50p, £1, £2, £2	Marconi
2002	8	1p, 2p, 5p, 10p, 20p, 50p, £1, £2	
2003	10	1p, 2p, 5p, 10p, 20p, 50p, 50p, £1, £2, £2	Women's Suffrage, DNA
2004	10	1p, 2p, 5p, 10p, 20p, 50p, 50p, £1, £2, £2	Bannister, Trevithick
2005	10	1p, 2p, 5p, 10p, 20p, 50p, 50p, £1, £2, £2	Dictionary, Guy Fawkes
2006	10	1p, 2p, 5p, 10p, 20p, 50p, 50p, £1, £2, £2	Victoria Cross, Brunel
2007	9	1p, 2p, 5p, 10p, 20p., 50p, £1, £2, £2	Slave trade, Act of Union
2008	7	1p - £1 old designs 'Emblems of Britain'	
2008	7	1p - £1 new designs	
2008	14	1p - £1 both designs	
2008	9	1p, 2p, 5p, 10p, 20p, 50p, £1, £2, £2	Old designs. Olympic £2.
2009	11	1p, 2p, 5p, 10p, 20p, 50p, 50p, £1, £2, £2, £2	Kew, Burns, Darwin.
2010	8	1p, 2p, 5p, 10,p 20p, 50p, £1, £2	
2011	13	1p, 2p, 5p, 10p, 20p, 50p, 50p, £1 x3, £2 x3	
2012	10	1p, 2p, 5p, 10p, 20p, 50p, £1, £2, £2, £5	
2013	15	1p, 2p, 5p, 10p, 20p, 50p x2, £1 x3, £2 x4, £5	
2014	14	1p, 2p, 5p, 10p, 20p, 50p x2, £1 x3, £2 x3, £5	
2015	13	1p,. 2p, 5p, 10p, 20p, 50p x2, £1, £2 x3, £5 x2	

The above sets tend to sell from between 2x to 4x the face value of the coins included. Sets in mint condition with absolutely no toning on any of the coins will attract a premium. At the time of writing the 2009 set is affected by the Kew Gardens 50p frenzy. See 50p Commemorative Type 13 for further details. 106,332 of the 2009 set were sold.

Year	Pieces	Coins
983	7	½p, 1p, 2p, 5p, 10p, 20p, 50p Specially packaged set for the H J Heinz Company.
983	8	½p, 1p, 2p, 5p, 10p, 20p, 50p, £1 Specially packaged set for the Martini & Rossi Company.
988	7	1p, 2p, 5p, 10p, 20p, 50p, £1 Special package celebrating Australia's Bicentennial.
996	14 (7+7)	1p, 2p, 5p, 10p, 20p, 50p, £1; pre-decimal 1/2d, 1d, 3d, 6d, 1/, 2/, 2/6d Special package commemorating 25 years of decimalisation.
2000	9	1p,2p,5p,10p,20p,50p,£1,£2, £5 (Millennium) In special "Time Capsule" packaging.
2004	3	50p (Roger Bannister), £1 (Forth bridge), £2 (Trevithick's Locomotive) "Celebrating Human Achievement"
2005	3	50p (Johnson's dictionary), £1 (Menai bridge), £2 (Guy Fawkes) new packaging of commemorative issues

The sets above were specially marketed for commemorative or promotional purposes. Other sets exist and will be included in a future edition.

INFO

1998 saw the introduction of yet another Royal Mint packaging, the "Baby Pack". These sets contain the same coins as the normal BU sets, but the packaging is oriented as gifts for newborn children, Continuing on this course, in 1999, the "Wedding Pack" was introduced.

The following are sterling (.925) silver proof sets, designed for various occasions, including the introduction of the coins themselves. These are normally found in hard acrylic capsules, enclosed in a clam-shell case, and with a certificate from the Royal Mint. Loose pieces, without the case and/or certificate, sell at a deep discount, up to 40% less. Some issues later than 1998 are included in the main section.

Five Pence
1990	35,000	large & small sized pair	£25.00

Ten Pence
1992	35,000	large & small sized pair	£25.00

Fifty Pence
1997	10,304	large & small sized pair	£25.00
1998	22,078	NHS issue and EU issue pair	£55.00
1998		pair, EU silver proof & EU silver Piedfort	£70.00

One Pound
1983 - 88	1,000	set of 6 regional designs, Arms, Shield	£75.00
1984 - 87	50,000	set of 4 regional designs	£90.00
1994 - 97	25,000	set of 4 regional designs	£100.00
1999 - 2002	25,000	set of 4 regional designs	£100.00

Two Pounds
1989	25,000	Bill of Rights & Claim of Rights pair	£60.00
1997	40,000	new bi-metallic circulation issue	£20.00
1998	25,000	new portrait on the circulation issue	£20.00
1997/98		bi-metallic Maklouf & Rank-Broadley pair	£35.00

1981	5,000	set, all issues, 1/2p-50p in base metals, sterling 25p commemorative, 22k gold Sovereign & £5	£700.00
1981		pair, sterling 25p commemorative, 22k gold Sovereign	£70.00
1992	1,000	set, both lg and sm 10p, 50p EEC, and £1	£75.00
1993	1,000	set, 50p EEC, £1, and £5 Coronation commem.	£75.00
1994	2,000	set, 50p D-Day, £1, and £2 Bank of England	£70.00
1995	1,000	silver set, peace £2, UN £2 and £1 coin	£50.00
1996	1,000	silver set, £5, £2 and £1 coins	£50.00
1996		set, all issues, 1p-£1 (25th Anniversary of Decimalisation)	£70.00
	500	pair, 1996 70th Birthday crown & 1997 Royal Wedding Jubilee crown	£60.00
1997		set, 50p, £1, £2, £5 Wedding Jubilee, £2 Britannia	£120.00
1999		set, £5 Millennium, £2 Britannia	£40.00
1999		set, £2 Britannia, £10 stamp	
2000	13,180	set, 1p-£5 Millennium, plus Maundy set (13 pieces)	£200.00
2000		£5 Millennium, plus YR2000 serial numbered £20 note	
		pair, 2002 Silver Jubilee crown & 2003 Coronation Jubilee crown	£60.00
2004		pair, 2004 Entente Cordiale crown & French €1 1/2 commem.	£75.00
2004	750	set, 50p Bannister, £1 Forth Bridge, £2 Trevithick, £5 Entente Cordiale £2 Britannia.	£75.00
asst'd		1999, 2001, 2002, 2003 £2 Britannia uncirculated.	£45.00

The following set was struck in .917 (22K) gold.

2002	2,002	set, 1p-£5 Golden Jubilee, plus Maundy set (13 pieces)	£750.00

ALERT

It seems that official Royal Mint cases were obtainable, and some of these sets were assembled on the secondary market, with the individual coins and accompanying certificates. Original RM-issued sets usually contain a single certificate, listing each coin in the set.

Piedforts are pieces that are double the thickness and weight of normal pieces, and are almost always struck in sterling (.925) silver. These are normally found in hard acrylic capsules, enclosed in a clam-shell case, and with a certificate from the Royal Mint. Loose pieces, without the case and/or certificate sell at a deep discount, up to 40% less.

Five Pence

1990	20,000	.925 sterling silver, small size Piedfort	£20.00

Ten Pence

1992		.925 sterling silver, small size Piedfort	£30.00

Twenty Pence

1982		.925 sterling silver, Piedfort	£30.00

Fifty Pence

1997	7,192	.925 sterling silver, small size Piedfort	£50.00
1998		EEC & NHS pair, Piedfort	£30.00

One Pound

1983 - 88	500	set of 6 regional designs, Arms, Shield, Piedfort	£250.00
1984 - 87	10,000	.925 sterling silver, proof set of 4 Piedfort	£175.00
1994 - 97		.925 sterling silver, proof set of 4 Piedfort	£190.00
1999-2002	10,000	.925 sterling silver, proof set of 4 Piedfort	£225.00
2004-2007	1,400	.925 sterling silver, proof set of 4 Piedfort	£200.00

Two Pounds

1989	10,000	Bill of Rights & Claim of Rights pair, Piedfort	£30.00
1997	10,000	.925 sterling silver, Piedfort	£55.00
1998	10,000	.925 sterling silver, Piedfort £55	
1997/98	.10,000	925 sterling silver, Piedfort (pair)	£125.00
1999	10,000	.925 sterling silver, proof Piedfort HOLOGRAM	£100.00

Five Pounds

2005		Nelson & Trafalgar pair, Piedfort	£125.00

ets

2003		set, 50p WPSU, £1 Royal Arms, £2 DNA Piedfort	£60.00
2004	7500	set, 50p Bannister, £1 Forth Bridge, £2 Trevithick Piedfort	£150.00
2005		set, 50p Johnson's Dictionary, £1 Menai Bridge, £2 GunPowder Plot, £2 World War II Piedfort	£150.00
2007		£5, both £2 coins, £1 and 50p Piedfort	£250.00
2008		2x £5 coins, £2 and £1 Piedfort	£250.00
2008		The 7 new Dent design coins as silver Piedforts	£350.00
2009		Piedfort gold proof set of 16x difference 50 pences	£ EXPENSIVE
2010		£5, £2, both £1 coins and the 50p	£300.00
2010/2011		Capital cities 4x £1 set	£300.00
2013		4x £5 coins, each with different Queen portrait	£683.00 new price
2013		The 5 Commemorative coins + the 2 £1 coins	£560.00 new price
2013		Pair of London Underground £2 coins	£200.00 new price
2014		The 4 Commemorative coins + the 2 £1 coins	£575.00 new price
2015		The 5 Commemoratice coins	£570.00 new price

pecial Collector Issues (Patterns)

A trial bi-metallic piece was issued in 1994 (predecessor to the £2 bi-metallic). The obverse shows a cutty (ship), while the reverse carries the Maklouf portrait of QEII. The ring bears the legend "ROYAL MINT TRIAL PATTERN", and an edge legend of 'ANNO REGNIA XLVI, DECUS ET TUTAMEN". See the £2 section.

attern sets issued by the Royal Mint to preview the new issue of "Bridges" £1 coins. All of these coins arry the date of 2003, and rather than having a face value, they are labelled as "PATTERN".

2003	7,500	.925 sterling silver, 7,500 , proof set of 4	£70.00
	3,000	.917 gold proof set of 4	£1000.00

A continuation of the above set, this set shows the "Beasts" series, which was a runner-up in the design competition for the new £1 coinage. All of these coins carry the date of 2004, and rather than having a face value, they are labelled as "PATTERN". Issued, as listed, in both sterling (.925) ilver, and 22k (.917) gold.

2004	5,000	.925 sterling silver, proof set of 4	£80.00
	2,250	.917 gold proof set of 4	£975.00

117

Silver Britannia issues began in 1997 with proof-only coins. Commencing in 1998, the RM has followed a pattern of using the standard Standing Britannia for every other year (even years) while bringing out new unique designs for the odd years. I believe the whole point of these Britannia issues was the fact that they were struck in Britannia silver (.9584 fine) which thought was the whole point of them. From 2013 the proof versions are it seems, now struck in .999 silver. I don't understand the logic behind that change.

In 2014 the RM have introduced another bullion range of coins, in .999 silver and also in .9999 gold. They are, according to the blurb: 'Celebrating Chinese and British heritage with a dynamic design'.

Bullion .958 Silver (UNC) £2 issues

1998	88,909	Standing Britannia	£23.00
1999	69,394	Britannia in Chariot	£23.00
2000	81,301	Standing Britannia	£23.00
2001	44,816	Una & the Lion	£23.00
2002	48,215	Standing Britannia	£23.00
2003	73,271	Helmeted Britannia facing left	£23.00
2004	100,000	Standing Britannia	£23.00
2005	100,000	Britannia seated	£23.00
2006		Standing Britannia	£23.00
2007		Britannia seated	£23.00
2008		Standing Britannia	£23.00
2009		Britannia standing in Chariot	£23.00
2010		Bust of Britannia in profile	£23.00
2011		Sitting Britannia	£23.00
2012		Standing Britannia	£23.00
2013		Standing Britannia	£23.00
2014		Standing Britannia	£25.00
2104	Mule error, with Lunar coin obverse (missing edge dentils)		£90.00

.958 Silver (PROOF) issues

1997	£2	4,173	Britannia in Chariot	£50.00
	20p	8,686		£20.00
1998	£2	2,168	Standing Britannia	£90.00
	20p	2,724		£20.00
2001	£2	3,047	Britannia with Lion	£60.00
	20p	826		£20.00
2003	£2	1,833	Britannia wearing Roman Helmet	£60.00
	20p	1,003		£20.00
2004	£2	5,000	Standing Britannia	£60.00
2005	£2	2,500	Britannia seated	£60.00
2006	£2	2,500	Standing Britannia	£60.00
2007	£2		Britannia seated	£60.00
	20p			£25.00

958 Silver (PROOF) issues

2008	20p	Standing Britannia	£60.00
	£2		£25.00
2009	£2	Britannia standing in Chariot	£70.00
2010	£2	Bust of Britannia in profile	£65.00
	20p		£25.00
2011	£2	Sitting Britannia	£60.00
	20p		£25.00
2012	£2	Standing Britannia	£50.00
	20p		£
2013	£2	Sitting Britiannia now .999	None available separately

Special (PROOF) sets

1997	11,832	Set of 4 (£2, £1, 50p, 20p)	£140.00
1998	3,044	Set of 4 (£2, £1, 50p, 20p)	£170.00
2001	4,596	Set of 4 (£2, £1, 50p, 20p)	£130.00
2003	3,623	Set of 4 (£2, £1, 50p, 20p)	£130.00
2005	5,000	Set of 4 (£2, £1, 50p, 20p)	£130.00
2006	-	Set of 5x different £2 with gold plated details	£210.00
2007	2,500	Set of 4 (£2, £1, 50p, 20p)	£130.00
2008		Set of 4 (£2, £1, 50p, 20p)	£170.00
2009		Set of 4 (£2, £1, 50p, 20p)	£150.00
2010		Set of 4 (£2, £1, 50p, 20p)	£150.00
2011		Set of 4 (£2, £1, 50p, 20p)	£180.00
2012		Set of 4 (£2, £1, 50p, 20p)	£250.00
2013	Now in .999 silver	Set of 5 (£2, £1, 50p, 20p, 10p)	£200.00 new price
		Pair of 20p and 10p	£37.50 new price

Platinum 2007 Coins were issued to mark the 20th Anniversary of the 'Britannia'

2007	£10		1/10 oz Platinum	£200.00
2007	£25		1/4 oz Platinum	£450.00
2007		250	Set of 4 Platinum coins	£3000.00

Lunar coins, proof issue prices (bullion versions tend to sell for about 2-2.5x bullion value)

2014	Horse design, 1 ounce proof .999 Silver see last page for picture	£82..50
	Mule error, with Britannia coin obverse (edge dentils present), value	£80.00
	Horse, 5 ounce proof .999 silver	£395.00
	Horse, 1 ounce .9999 gold	£1950.00
2015	Sheep design, 1 ounce proof .999 silver	£82.50
	Sheep design, 1 ounce proof .9999 gold	£1950.00
	Sheep design, 5 ounce proof .999 Silver	£395.00
	Sheep design, 5 ounce proof .9999 gold	£7500.00

Gold Britannia issues began in 1987, as both bullion issues as well as proof issue The values of the bullion issues are based on the value of the gold content, which fluctuates dail The prices for these issues are given only as a guideline.

Bullion .917 Gold (UNC) Issues

£10	tenth ounce	Bullion Value + 30 to 50%
£25	quarter ounce	Bullion Value + 12 to 25%
£50	half ounce	Bullion Value + 8 to 20%
£100	one ounce	Bullion Value + 5 to 15%

The following are 4-piece sets, each coin encapsulated, and housed in a clamshell case,.

Special PROOF sets of 4 coins (for some dates, 3 or 5 coin sets were issued)

1987	10,000	Britannia standing	£1900.00
1988	3,505	Britannia standing	£1925.00
1989	2,268	Britannia standing	£2000.00
1990	527	Britannia standing	£1950.00
1991	509	Britannia standing	£1900.00
1992	500	Britannia standing	£1900.00
1993	462	Britannia standing	£1925.00
1994	435	Britannia standing	£1950.00
1995	500	Britannia standing	£2000.00
1996	483	Britannia standing	£2000.00
1997	892	Britannia standing	£2000.00
1998	750	Britannia standing	£2000.00
1999	750	Britannia standing	£2050.00
2000	750	Britannia standing	£2000.00
2001	1,000	Una & the Lion	£2000.00
2002	945	Britannia standing	£1700.00
2003	1,250	Britannia with Helmet	£1700.00
2004	973	Britannia standing	£1700.00
2005	1,439	Britannia seated	£1700.00
2006	1,163	Britannia standing	£1700.00
2007	1,250	Britannia seated	£1700.00
2008	1,250	Britannia standing	£1700.00
2009		Britannia standing in chariot	£1700.00
2010		Britannia bust in profile	£2200.00
2011		4 coin set	£2500.00
		3 coin set	£1300.00
2012		Britannia standing	£2200.00
2013		Now .9999 gold	£2900.00 new price
		3 coin set	£
2014		6 coin set	£2600.00 new price
2014		3 coin set	£1175.00 new price

ritannia (PROOF) invividual cased coins

00	1997	£1000.00
100	Other dates	£850.00-£1000.00
50	All dates	£450.00-£600.00
25	All dates	£230.00-£350.00
10	All dates	Around £100.00-£150.00

Gold Sovereign-based single coins are defined as non-commemorative Five Pounds, Two Pounds, Sovereigns and Half Sovereigns struck to normal or proof standards and sold singularly as gold bullion coins or as proof collectors' coins. The non-proof coins do not have boxes or certificates and are normally just traded as gold. Sovereigns and half sovereigns are 22 carat gold (.917 fine) and weigh 7.98g and 3.97g respectively.

Five Pounds

1984	Cased proof only	£1200.00
1984	Cased proof only with 'U' in circle next to date	£1100.00
1985	Cased proof only	£1200.00
1985	with 'U' in circle next to date	£1100.00
1986	with 'U' in circle next to date	£1100.00
1987	with 'U' in circle next to date	£1100.00
1988	with 'U' in circle next to date	£1100.00
1989	Sovereign Anniversary type	£1200.00
1989	Sovereign Anniversary type, cased proof	£1300.00
1990	with 'U' in circle next to date	£1150.00
1991	with 'U' in circle next to date	£1150.00
1992	with 'U' in circle next to date	£1150.00
1993	with 'U' in circle next to date	£1150.00
1994	with 'U' in circle next to date	£1150.00
1995	with 'U' in circle next to date	£1150.00
1996	with 'U' in circle next to date	£1150.00
1997	with 'U' in circle next to date	£1200.00
1998	New portrait	£1200.00
1999		£1200.00
2000		£1200.00
2000	with 'U' in circle next to date	£1200.00
2001		£1200.00
2002	Shield reverse	£1200.00
2003 to 2010		£1300.00
2011		£1600.00
2012		£1600.00
2013 to 2015		£2000.00

Two Pounds (double sovereign)

All are cased proofs. The £2 coin has not often been issued on its own.

1987		£300.00
1988		£300.00
1989	Sovereign Anniversary type	£350.00
1990		£300.00
1991		£300.00
1992		£300.00
1993		£300.00
1994	(see 1994 error commemorative type 4 £2 coin)	
1996		£300.00

Sovereigns, loose bullion type

Sovereigns of the 1970s and 1980s are generally traded at their bullion value. They contain 7.32 grammes of fine gold. Particularly perfect examples may be worth a slight premium. The dates struck were as follows:

1974, 1976, 1978, 1979, 1980, 1981 and 1982   Bullion Value

Modern bullion type sovereigns, from 2000 to date, tend to sell for a little more than bullion value as follows:

£180.00 to £230.00

Sovereigns, cased proof type

1979		£200.00
1980		£200.00
1981		£200.00
1982		£200.00
1983		£200.00
1984		£210.00
1985		£220.00
1986		£210.00
1987		£210.00
1988		£220.00
1989	500th Anniversary of the Sovereign	£600.00
1990		£240.00
1991		£240.00
1992		£250.00
1993		£250.00
1994		£250.00
1995		£250.00
1996		£250.00
1997		£250.00
1998		£250.00
1999		£250.00
2000		£250.00
2001		£260.00
2002		£260.00
2003		£260.00
2004		£260.00
2005 to 2013		£260.00
2014		£300.00
2015		£300.00

Half Sovereigns, loose bullion type

Until recently, the 1982 Half Sovereign was the only non-proof coin and continues to trade at approximately bullion value. In 2000 the Royal Mint started issuing non-proof half sovereigns and have done so each year since. The 2000 to 2007 half sovereigns tend to trade from about £100 to £120 (based on the bullion value at the time of writing). The shield reverse 2002 coin and the St. George 2005 coin are the most popular.

Half Sovereigns, cased proof type

1979		£100.00
1980		£100.00
1981		£100.00
1982		£100.00
1983		£100.00
1984		£100.00
1985		£100.00
1986		£100.00
1987		£100.00
1988		£100.00
1989	500th Anniversary of the Sovereign	£200.00
1990		£120.00
1991		£120.00
1992		£130.00
1993		£130.00
1994		£130.00
1995		£130.00
1996		£130.00
1997		£130.00
1998		£130.00
1999		£130.00
2000		£130.00
2001		£130.00
2002		£140.00
2003		£140.00
2004		£130.00
2005		£130.00
2006		£140.00
2007		£140.00
2008 to 2013		£150.00
2014 (also 2014 I - India mint)		£150.00
2015 (2015 I? Not seen)		£150.00

Quarter Sovereigns

Introduced in 2009 as a made-up denomination (quarter of a sovereign is a crown, isn't it?) - they seem to sell for £60 - £100, both bullion and proof issue.

?80	10,000	£5, £2, Sovereign (£1), 1/2 Sovereign	£1700.00
?81	-	Set containing 9 coins including silver Crown	£1000.00
?82	2,500	£5, £2, Sovereign (£1), 1/2 Sovereign	£1700.00
?83		£2, Sovereign (£1), 1/2 Sovereign	£900.00
?84	7,095	£5, Sovereign (£1), 1/2 Sovereign	£1350.00
?85	5,849	£5, £2, Sovereign (£1), 1/2 Sovereign	£1800.00
?86	12,000	£2 Commonwealth Games, Sovereign (£1), 1/2 Sovereign	£1000.00
?87	12,500	£2, Sovereign (£1), 1/2 Sovereign	£850.00
?88	12,500	£2, Sovereign (£1), 1/2 Sovereign	£950.00
?89	5,000	£5, £2, Sovereign (£1), 1/2 Sovereign (Anniversary reverse)	£3000.00
	7,936	£2, Sovereign (£1), 1/2 Sovereign (Anniversary reverse)	£2000.00
?90	1,721	£5, £2, Sovereign (£1), 1/2 Sovereign	£2000.00
	1,937	£2, Sovereign (£1), 1/2 Sovereign	£1000.00
?91	1,336	£5, £2, Sovereign (£1), 1/2 Sovereign	£2000.00
	1,152	£2, Sovereign (£1), 1/2 Sovereign	£1000.00
?92	1,165	£5, £2, Sovereign (£1), 1/2 Sovereign	£2000.00
	967	£2, Sovereign (£1), 1/2 Sovereign	£1000.00
?93	1,078	£5, £2, Sovereign (£1), 1/2 Sovereign (Pistrucci medallion)	£2200.00
	663	£2, Sovereign (£1), 1/2 Sovereign	£1200.00
?94	918	£5, £2 (Bank of England), Sovereign (£1), 1/2 Sovereign	£2000.00
	1,249	£2 (Bank of England), Sovereign (£1), 1/2 Sovereign	£1100.00
?95	718	£5, £2 (Dove of Peace), Sovereign (£1), 1/2 Sovereign	£2000.00
	1,112	£2 (Dove of Peace), Sovereign (£1), 1/2 Sovereign	£1200.00
?96	742	£5, £2, Sovereign (£1), 1/2 Sovereign	£2000.00
	868	£2, Sovereign (£1), 1/2 Sovereign	£1200.00
?97	860	£5, £2 (bi-metallic), Sovereign (£1), 1/2 Sovereign	£2000.00
	817	£2 (bi-metallic), Sovereign (£1), 1/2 Sovereign	£1200.00
?98	789	£5, £2, Sovereign (£1), 1/2 Sovereign	£2000.00
	560	£2, Sovereign (£1), 1/2 Sovereign	£1100.00
?99	991	£5, £2 (Rugby World Cup), Sovereign (£1), 1/2 Sovereign	£2000.00
	912	£2 (Rugby World Cup), Sovereign (£1), 1/2 Sovereign	£1300.00
?000	1,000	£5, £2, Sovereign (£1), 1/2 Sovereign	£2100.00
	1,250	£2, Sovereign (£1), 1/2 Sovereign	£1200.00

2001	1,000	£5, £2 (Marconi), Sovereign (£1), 1/2 Sovereign	£2100.00
	891	£2 (Marconi), Sovereign (£1), 1/2 Sovereign	£1200.00
2002	3,000	£5, £2, Sovereign (£1), 1/2 Sovereign (Shield reverse)	£2400.00
	3,947	£2, Sovereign (£1), 1/2 Sovereign.(Shield reverse)	£1400.00
2003	2,250	£5, £2, Sovereign (£1), 1/2 Sovereign	£2000.00
	1,717	£2 (DNA), Sovereign (£1), 1/2 Sovereign	£1100.00
2004	2,250	£5, £2, Sovereign (£1), 1/2 Sovereign	£2000.00
	2,500	£2, £1 (Forth Bridge), 1/2 Sovereign	£1100.00
2005	1,500	£5, £2, Sovereign (£1), 1/2 Sovereign	£2100.00
	2,500	£2, Sovereign (£1), 1/2 Sovereign	£1100.00
2006	1,750	£5, £2, Sovereign (£1), 1/2 Sovereign	£2000.00
	1,750	£2, Sovereign (£1), 1/2 Sovereign	£1200.00
2007		Sovereign, 1/2 Sovereign	£450.00
	700	£2, Sovereign, 1/2 Sovereign	£1200.00
2008		Sovereign, 1/2 Sovereign	£450.00
		£5, £2, Sovereign, 1/2 Sovereign	£2000.00
		£2, Sovereign, 1/2 Sovereign	£1100.00
2009		£5, £2, Sovereign, 1/2 Sovereign and new 1/4 Sovereign	£2400.00
		£2, Sovereign, 1/2 Sovereign and new 1/4 Sovereign	£1050.00
2010		£5, £2, Sovereign, 1/2 Sovereign, 1/4 Sovereign. Issue price	£2550.00
		Sovereign, 1/2 Sovereign, 1/4 Sovereign. Issue price	£550.00
		'Premium' set, 3 coins as above. Issue price	£1030.00

Values of later sets are similar. They are a lot more expensive when bought new.

Based on a tradition dating back to the 12th century, every year on Maundy Thursday (the day before Good Friday), the monarch distributes leather pouches of special coins to selected people in a Royal Ceremony. The number of recipients is equal to the age of the monarch, as is the value of the coins in each pouch.

All Maundy coinage issued under the reign of Queen Elizabeth II carries the same obverse portrait, that of the first bust of the Queen used on coins and designed by Mary Gillick.

Prices listed here are for complete sets in official Royal Mint cases, which became standard in the 1960s. Commencing in 1989, the coins are individually encapsulated within the case.

1971	1,018	Tewkesbury Abbey	£120.00
1972	1,026	York Minster	£130.00
1973	1,004	Westminster Abbey	£120.00
1974	1,042	Salisbury Cathedral	£120.00
1975	1,050	Peterborough Cathedral	£120.00
1976	1,158	Hereford Cathedral	£120.00
1977	1,138	Westminster Abbey	£120.00
1978	1,178	Carlisle Cathedral	£120.00
1979	1,188	Winchester Cathedral	£120.00
1980	1,198	Worcester Cathedral	£120.00
1981	1,178	Westminster Abbey	£120.00
1982	1,218	St. David's Cathedral, Dyfed	£120.00
1983	1,228	Exeter Cathedral	£120.00
1984	1,238	Southwell Minster	£120.00
1985	1,248	Ripon Cathedral	£130.00
1986	1,378	Chichester Cathedral	£120.00
1987	1,390	Ely Cathedral	£120.00
1988	1,402	Lichfield Cathedral	£120.00
1989	1,353	Birmingham Cathedral	£120.00
1990	1,523	Newcastle Cathedral	£120.00
1991	1,384	Westminster Abbey	£120.00
1992	1,424	Chester Cathedral	£120.00
1993	1,440	Wells Cathedral	£120.00
1994	1,433	Truro Cathedral	£120.00

INFO

On "Decimalisation Day" in 1971, all Maundy money was re-valued to decimal pence (the old 1d pieces became worth 1p decimal). Since 1971, the coins have the face value of 1p, 2p, 3p, 4p although there is no significant change in design to note this transition.

127

1995	1,466	Coventry Cathedral	£120.00
1996	1,629	Norwich Cathedral	£120.00
1997	1,786	Bradford Cathedral	£130.00
1998	1,654	Portsmouth Cathedral	£120.00
1999	1,676	Bristol Cathedral	£120.00
2000	1,684	Lincoln Cathedral	£120.00
2000	13,180	silver proof set, taken from special "Millennium Proof Set" listed on pg. 69	£120.00
2001	1,706	Westminster Abbey	£120.00
2002	1,678	Canterbury Cathedral	£120.00
2002	2,002	gold proof set, taken from special "Golden Jubilee Proof Set".	£1100.00
2003		Gloucester Cathedral	£120.00
2004		Liverpool (Anglican) Cathedral	£120.00
2005		Wakefield Cathedral	£120.00
2006		Guildford Cathedral	£150.00
2007		Manchester Cathedral	
2008		St. Patricks Cathedral, Armagh	
2009		St. Edmundsbury Cathedral, Suffolk	
2010		Derby Cathederal	
2011		Westminster Abbey	
2012		York Minster	
2013		Christ Church Cathedral, Oxford	
2014		Blackburn Cathedral	

The Lunar series 2014 Horse design by Wuon-Gean Ho,
as featured on page 113.

The Cover Images.

The images on the cover of this book have a Winston Churchill theme. Shown are (right) the 2010 Churchill coin from the "Celebration of Britain" 18-coin collection, the 2015 silver £20 (left) coin and the 2015 £5 crown (bottom).